D1451894

Found On
Charm Square
Azur-ite (Blue)
Swirl

Found On All
Forest Green
Glassware

Found Only On
Turquoise Blue
Dinnerware

Found On
22K Gold
Dinnerware

Found Only
On Royal Ruby
Glassware

farca

HOUSTON PUBLIC LIBRARY

. R01007 79701

HOUSTON PUBLIC LIBRARY

. R01007 79701

U.S. $24.95

A Collector's Guide To Anchor Hocking's

"Fire-King"
Glassware

1st Edition

By: Garry & Dale Kilgo
Jerry & Gail Wilkins

Fully Illustrated, Most in Full Color, Current Price Guide

K & W Collectibles Publisher

Copyright 1991 by Garry Kilgo, and Jerry Wilkins, exclusive publishing and marketing rights K&W Collectibles, P.O. Box 473 Addison, Alabama 35540. All rights reserved. No part of the book may be used or reproduced in any manner whatsoever, except in the case of brief quotations embodied in critical articles or reviews.

"50 YEARS OF FIRE-KING"
(1942-1992)

To commemorate the 50th. year of Anchor Hocking's "Fire-King" glassware. Anchor Hocking has introduced two special edition items, a 9" pie plate and a two cup measuring cup. The 9" pie plate is crystal clear with two large tab handles and a pinched pie crust style rim. The bottom is embossed with very large print that reads, Commemorating 50 years Fire-King (anchor over H symbol) and in smaller print, ANCHOR OVENWARE USA H1075 PIE PLATE 9 IN. DIA. OVEN & MICROWAVE SAFE NO STOVE TOP OR BROILER USE. The measuring cup is crystal clear with red lettering that gives measurements up to 2 cups, 16 ozs., 1 pint, ½ litre, 500 mls. and 5 dls. On the front of the cup in large red print is, Commemorating 50 years Fire-King (anchor over H symbol). The bottom is embossed, COOKING USE ONLY USA (mold #) (modern style anchor symbol) Anchor Hocking (item #) MICROWAVE SAFE.

If you are a serious Fire-King collector these will make a very attractive addition to your collection. They are in very limited supply so you had better get them while the last. They retail for just under two dollars, you just can't beat that these days.

ACKNOWLEDGMENTS

There have been so many wonderful people who have given us their time and knowledge so unselfishly, that if we had the space and time to acknowledge them all it would be a book in it's self. We will try to thank as many as space and memory will allow, and if we should forget to mention anyone please know that we sincerely appreciate all that you have done to make this book become a reality.

First of all we would like to thank the "Good Lord" for giving us the strength and courage to see this task through. As you know there are four authors of this book and each have contributed equally, and without this group effort the completion of this book would not have been possible.

Next we would like thank all the great people at Anchor Hocking for their genuine interest in the preservation of the history of their glass. These people have gone out of their way in helping us, by loaning us the use of their old catalogs and sales material, to allowing us to examine first hand the priceless glass in the "Old Glass Morgue". Individually we would like to thank Phil Bee for giving us the tour of the morgue and the list of production dates. We can't begin to express our gratitude to a very special lady at Anchor Hocking, Barbara Wolf. She has taken the time she really didn't have, to answer our many questions. We were allowed to research the old catalogs with the help of Beckey Morris, who dug through files to find the information we needed. These are the kind of people who have made Anchor Hocking one of the most successful glassware companies in America.

We can't forget the collectors and dealers with whom we have shared our love for the glassware listed in this book. When we get a chance to attend the Nashville Tenn. Fairgrounds Fleamarket we always look up these dealers. They really know their "FIRE-KING". The "First Lady" is Glenda Hunt. She always has loads of "FIRE-KING" and a great big smile that will make your day. Then there's Sharon and Tom Oakley from Newburgh, Indiana. Along with tons of "FIRE-KING" you will find that Sharon is very knowledgeable on her glass. Don't go trying to sell her on the idea "Copper-tint" is the correct name for "Peach Lustre". Believe me you'll have some crow to eat. Also on Memorial Day and Labor Day weekends we look for a booth with about ten tables full of 40's and 50's glass and there you will find Mrs. Don Whaley. This fine lady seems to have all of the hard to find pieces of "FIRE-KING" we are looking for.

When we get a chance to attend the glass shows in our area we look up these people. We enjoy not only the glass they sell but the warm and friendly conversation as well. Thank you Bill and Lenette Heidlman of Rosenburg, Texas for the Oxadol Soap coupon and all your encouragement. Thanks to Jack and Joyce Nichols, Peggy Nobles, Tom and Jean Niner, Lynn and Faye Strait and all the other dealers at the many Glass Shows we have attended and the geniune interest you have all shown in this book. Also many thanks to all the antique shops and mall dealers who have been so helpful with this project. In Lancaster, Ohio thank you Gloria Reynolds, and Veryleen Summers of Broad St. Antiques for all your help. Thanks also goes to David and Tammy Eddy of Wheelbarrow Antiques in Decatur, Al. for the help in finding some of the glass used in this book. Thank you Tela Bearden of Tela's Old and New Shop in Palmerdale, Al. for all the glass and for sharing your many years of glass collecting.

A very special thanks to Ruth Bradford of Bryan Publications for having so much patience with these first time authors. Without her help we would have long ago given up on ever putting this book together. Thanks also Michelle Sandlin for the photography work and the seemingly endless hours of waiting for us to set each shot up of each set of glassware before she could take the picture. And thank you to all the people of The Cullman Times for all their hard work, trying to make sense of what we had written.

The next thank you is for Carla Taylor of Rose Printing Co., Tallahassee, Fl., because of her knowledge and experience she has made each step of the actual printing go much more smoothly than we ever expected. Also a word of thanks to Albert Partridge and Fay Cobbs for the financial and legal assistance necessary in making this book a reality.

Because of these and many more individuals, you now have this beautiful book to use, and to enjoy on each of your own "FIRE-KING" glassware expeditions.

FOREWORD

The glassware we will cover in this book carries the "FIRE-KING" trademark of Anchor Hocking Glass Corp. of Lancaster Ohio, and was produced from 1942-1976. Anchor Hocking introduced a formula of heat-proof glass which was so durable they guaranteed it against breakage due to heat for two years. To identify it from the other glassware on the market they embossed each piece with the name "FIRE-KING". This trademark is found embossed on about 90% of this glassware with the remaining 10% having labels attached that identified it as "FIRE-KING" glassware. In this line of glassware Anchor Hocking introduced some of it's most popular colors, JADE-ITE, IVORY, ROYAL RUBY, FOREST GREEN, AZUR-ITE, MILK WHITE, and TURQUOISE BLUE, along with many fired on colors and floral patterns on milk white glass.

"FIRE-KING" was one of the least expensive lines of glassware on the market in it's day. This, along with it's simple beauty, is probably the reason it was so widely used as premiums by so many different companies. This is also one of the reasons you can almost always find at least one piece of "FIRE-KING" glassware or ovenware in any kitchen cabinet in the U.S.A.

We hope this book will help you identify each pattern and piece that was produced during the "FIRE-KING" years at Anchor Hocking. We have spent 6 years and many thousand miles in collecting the information you will find in this book. From the many flea markets, antique shops, malls, and libraries to the catalogs, records, files and archieves of Anchor Hocking. We have found much information, yet we still find something new with every trip.

As for the way we compiled the price guides, we used an average of the prices found on each piece, from flea markets, antique shops, and malls to the many glass shows across the country. We did not include yard sales or thrift shops as we felt their prices did not reflect the true value of collectible glassware. We also found that pricing on some items are regional in respect to the availability of that particular item. There is also a continuing need for updating the prices due to ever increasing number of collectors who are including "FIRE-KING" in their collections. (In just the last 5 years) prices have increased ten fold as "FIRE-KING" has slowly emerged from the ranks of junk dishes to a very desirable collectible. As with all collectibles the price one pays is the price he or she is willing and able to pay to complete a particular set.

The measurements used are the ones listed in Anchor Hocking's catalogs and sales brochures. If we could not find them in this manner, we took the measurements and rounded them off to the nearest 1/8".

The pricing in this book is for a guide only and should not be used to set prices,due to varying prices from one section of the country to another. Also the condition of a piece of glassware will be an important factor in the price. Neither the Authors nor the Publisher assumes responsibility for any losses that may be incurred as a result of consulting this book.

TABLE OF CONTENTS

1976-Present

Anchor Corporate Symbol Contemporary

Anchor Hocking's corporate symbol has evolved through the company's 75 years, undergoing periodic change to keep pace with a changing world.

The current symbol — the bold, blue anchor of modern design — reflects Anchor Hocking as a "growing, contemporary" company in tune with the times, according to James A. Biggerstaff, vice president, administrative services.

The symbol and new logotype were chosen in 1976 to replace the red Anchor-H as part of an on-going corporate identification program designed to increase consumer awareness of Anchor Hocking and its many products.

"The new symbol provides a much more effective portrayal of the dynamic image we want to convey," Biggerstaff said.

"The prior one was effective for its time, but with changes in our environment it became less descriptive of the company we have become."

The traditional Anchor-H identified Anchor Hocking since 1937 when it was created to illustrate the merger of The Hocking Glass Company and Anchor Cap Corporation.

As a result of a 1975-76 study of corporate identity graphics, J. Ray Topper, current president and chief operating officer, found that a lack of uniformity had resulted in many varieties of the basic symbol being used.

"The symbol didn't have the meaning it was supposed to have," Biggerstaff explained. "What was the right version? Everybody had his and her own idea of what it ought to be."

In an effort to evaluate further our corporate identity, Anchor Hocking commissioned a design

1937-1976

**Anchor Cap Corp.
-1937**

**Hocking Glass Co.
1905-1937**

study and marketplace survey by an industrial design concern.

The study and survey confirmed what was already suspected: "People didn't have the opinion of Anchor Hocking we wanted them to have," according to Biggerstaff.

The industrial design concern recommended that Anchor Hocking upgrade its corporate identity as perceived by consumers, employees and others.

The concern presented elements of the now famous corporate identification program to a task force comprised of Anchor Hocking managers.

Biggerstaff says the program h permitted Anchor Hocking to present a unified look when communicating with the company's various "publics."

The new symbol has been gradually incorporated on all packaging, stationery, forms and advertising materials.

Full implementation will probably take "several more years," Biggerstaff says.

Identity coordinators interpret guidelines to insure all changes are made in conformity with a manual developed by the task force. "We can't allow uniformity to be jeopardized," Biggerstaff says. "It works out very well."

The goal is to use the symbol in all Anchor Hocking's divisions and subsidiaries, bringing a "family" identification to company activities and products.

Biggerstaff sees no further design changes in the foreseeable future for the company's new symbol and logotype.

He concludes, "From today's perspective, I see no need for a further change in application, but time will tell. As times and the company change, we expect to change with them."

HISTORY

In 1905 Isaac J. Collins started the "Hocking Glass Company", named after the Hocking River near Lancaster Ohio. The building was purchased from a carbon company whose operations had left the building black with soot. The townspeople called the plant the "Black Cat".

On March 6, 1924 a fire completely destroyed the plant. No one knew how the fire started, but by morning, all that was left was five acres of ash and rubble. Just six short months after the fire, a new plant had been erected and was in operation.

By 1928, Hocking was making a complete line of pressed dinnerware in an attractive green color, along with other items too numerous to mention. By the 1930's green along with the colors of pale blue, and pink became even more popular. Many different patterns of glassware were made during this period, which we know as the "Depression Era". Some of the most beautiful glassware ever made, was made during those days. When many plants and factories were closing their doors, Hocking Glass managed to survive those hard times.

In 1937 the Hocking Glass Company merged with the Anchor Cap Corporation, and changed the name of the company to the "Anchor Hocking Glass Corporation". It was after this merger that a new mixture of glass, that would not crack or break when placed in an oven at high temperatures, went into production.

Production of glassware marked "FIRE-KING" began around 1942 and continued until 1976. Beautiful colors of jade-ite, turqouise blue, azur-ite, pink, gray, lustre, blue, white, and ivory, along with dots, stripes, and floral designs were made during these years. "FIRE-KING," truly a pattern of glassware with a style of it's own, will represent a large portion of the next generation of collectible glassware.

"ALICE"
(1940's)
G-5000

"Alice" (G5000 line) is a pattern of glassware that would have been a highly collectible pattern, if only there had been more items made. In 1945, Quaker Oats Co. placed an order with Anchor Hocking for some items to be used as premiums in boxes of oats. Unfortunately, only three items were made to fill this order. This included a 9" plate, a cup and saucer. The plate was packed in a larger box of oats, which probably was purchased less often than the smaller box. This could be one reason why the plates are harder to find than the cups and saucers.

Anchor Hocking made this pattern in jade-ite, white, ivory, white with red trimmed edges, and white with blue trimmed edges. Just off center in the plates and saucers will be a noticeable ribbed design, and further up on the rim will be a floral design. The cup has a floral design around the top of the outside, and a ribbed design from there down to the bottom.

Trademarks of this pattern are: (OVEN Fire-King GLASS), (anchor over the letter H), and bullseye design, with heavy ribbed design around the edge).

Trying to collect this pattern will not be an easy task. It took four years to find a white plate trimmed in blue that was in mint condition. The jade-ite plates are a little easier found, along with the cups and saucers in both patterns.

PRICE GUIDE

DESCRIPTION			CURRENT PRICES
CUP	- 8 oz.	(Jade-Ite)	— $4.50
SAUCER	- 5 7/8"	(Jade-Ite)	— 3.00
PLATE	- 8 ½"	(Jade-Ite)	— 12.00
CUP	- 8 oz.	(White/Blue Trim)	— 5.00
		(White/Red Trim)	— 5.00
SAUCER	- 5 7/8"	(White/Blue Trim)	— 3.00
		(White/Red Trim)	— 3.00
PLATE	- 8 ½"	(White/Red Trim)	— 15.00

PRICE GUIDE

DESCRIPTION			CURRENT PRICES
PLATE	- 8 ½"	(White/Blue Trim)	— $15.00
		(White/Red Trim)	— 13.00
CUP	- 8 oz.	(Ivory)	— 4.00
SAUCER	- 5 7/8"	(Ivory)	— 2.50
PLATE	- 8 ½"	(Ivory)	— 11.00
CUP	- 8 oz.	(White/Red Trim)	— 5.00
SAUCER	- 5 7/8"	(White/Red Trim)	— 3.00

"ANNIVERSARY ROSE" 60TH
(1964-1965)
W4600/60

"Anniversary Rose" is identified by it's milk-white color and a pair of two tone pink roses with green leaves and black stems in the center of each piece. Also the edge of each piece is trimmed with 22k gold.

The hard to find pieces are almost everything! Due to it's very short run, or to it's beauty, whichever, there just isn't very much of it showing up at the flea markets and antique malls, yet!

The trademark found on this pattern is (OVEN Fire-King WARE MADE IN U.S.A.).

PRICE GUIDE

DESCRIPTION		CURRENT PRICES
CUP	- 8 oz.	— $3.00
SAUCER	- 5 ¾"	— 1.00
PLATE, SALAD	- 7 3/8"	— 3.00
PLATE, DINNER	- 10"	— 5.00
PLATTER, OVAL	- 9"x 12"	— 6.00
BOWL, DESSERT	- 4 5/8"	— 3.00
BOWL, SOUP	- 6 5/8"	— 5.00
BOWL, VEGETABLE	- 8 ¼"	— 6.00
SUGAR, LID*	-	— 4.00
CREAMER	-	— 4.00

*Sugar without lid deduct $1.00.

W4679/29

W4629/29

W4678/29

W4674/29　　　W4667/29

W4647/29

W4638/29　　　W4646/29

W4653/29

W4654/29

anniversary rose
dinnerware

Heat-resistant, translucent white with a delicate rose design, and ringed with 22K gold. Open stock or gift sets. A real charmer!

			Doz. Ctn.	Lbs. Ctn.
W4679/29	8 oz	cup	3	14
W4629/29	5¾″	saucer	3	14
W4674/29	4⅝″	dessert	3	11
W4638/29	7⅜″	salad plate	3	23
W4667/29	6⅝″	soup plate	3	25
W4646/29	10″	dinner plate	3	44
W4678/29	8¼″	vegetable bowl	1	14
W4647/29	12 x 9″	platter	1	20
W4653/29		sugar/cover	1	9
W4654/29		creamer	1	7

Packed Sets		Sets Ctn.	Lbs. Ctn.
W4600/63	16 pc starter set, display ctn., 4 cups, 4 saucers, 4 desserts, 4 dinner plates	4	38
W4600/64	35 pc set, 6 cups, 6 saucers, 6 desserts, 6 soups, 6 dinner plates, vegetable, platter, sugar/cover, creamer	1	23
W4600/65	45 pc dinner set, 8 cups, 8 saucers, 8 desserts, 8 dinner plates, 8 soups, vegetable, platter, sugar/cover, creamer	1	30
W4600/67	53 pc dinner set, 8 cups, 8 saucers, 8 desserts, 8 soups, 8 dinner plates, 8 salad plates, vegetable, platter, sugar/cover, creamer	1	34

milk-white sauce/gravy boat

New, all-white; also goes beautifully with Wheat or Golden Shell. Heat-retaining milk-white glass keeps gravy warm.

			Doz. Ctn.	Lbs. Ctn.
W114	11½ oz	sauce/gravy boat	1	11

W114

39

5

"BLUE & GOLD FLORAL"
(1962)
W4600

As of this writing we have not found this pattern listed in any of Anchor Hocking's catalogs, or magazine ads. So the name we are using is of our own making. This is the most attractive floral pattern of the W4600 line of tableware. This may account for it not being found in flea markets, antique shops, and malls at the present time.

The trademarks used on this set are, (OVEN Fire-King ware, mold #, MADE IN U.S.A.), and (ANCHOR HOCKING [anchor over H symbol] Fire-King WARE, mold #, MADE IN U.S.A.). By using the trademarks, and the fact this set uses the 10" plate we have dated this set between the early and mid 60's.

The hard to find pieces at the present time, are almost everything in this pattern. But in time we feel it will begin to show up as it's popularity grows.

PRICE GUIDE

DESCRIPTION		CURRENT PRICES
CUP	- 8 oz.	— $3.00
SAUCER	- 5 ¾"	— 2.00
PLATE, SALAD	- 7 3/8"	— 3.00
PLATE, DINNER	- 10"	— 6.00
PLATTER, OVAL	- 9"x 12"	— 8.00
BOWL, DESSERT	- 4 5/8"	— 4.00
BOWL, SOUP	- 6 5/8"	— 5.00
BOWL, VEGETABLE	- 8 ¼"	— 10.00
SUGAR, OPEN	-	— 5.00
CREAMER	-	— 5.00
MUG	- 8 oz.	— 3.00

*Sugar Without Lid Deduct $1.00

"BLUE MOSAIC"
(1966-1968)
W4600/71

"Blue Mosaic" is still a young pattern of "FIRE-KING" that's finally beginning to emerge among other collectable glassware. Trying to find it now is no easy task, but maybe time will bring more of it out into the open.

The saucer and lid to the sugar are solid white. All the plates, the platter, and the bowls are white with a blue mosaic pattern in the center of each piece. The snack set plate has a cup indent on one end, and the mosaic design on the other. The cup, creamer, and sugar have a fired on blue color with white bottoms. This is also the first dinnerware set to use the 7½ oz. stacking cups.

The trademarks found on this pattern are, (OVEN Fire-King WARE MADE IN THE U.S.A.) or (ANCHOR HOCKING OVEN Fire-King WARE MADE IN THE U.S.A.).

PRICE GUIDE

DESCRIPTION		CURRENT PRICES
CUP, STACKING	- 7 ½ oz.	— $3.00
SAUCER	- 5 ¾"	— 1.00
PLATE, SALAD	- 7 3/8"	— 3.00
PLATE, DINNER	- 10"	— 4.00
PLATTER, OVAL	- 9"x 12"	— 6.00
BOWL, DESSERT	- 4 5/8"	— 3.00
BOWL, SOUP	- 6 5/8"	— 5.00
BOWL, VEGETABLE	- 8 ¼"	— 6.00
SUGAR & LID*	-	— 4.00
CREAMER	-	— 3.00
PLATE, SNACK SET, OVAL	-	— 3.00
CUP, SNACK SET, STACKING	-	— 3.00

*Sugar without lid deduct $1.00.

DINNERWARE

Growth stock. Declared a sound
investment by women with a knack
for setting bright tables.

BLUE MOSAIC

W4638/71

W4674/71

W4646/71

W4659/6623   W4649

BLUE MOSAIC
(heat resistant)

OPEN STOCK

	CARTON		PRICE
	Doz.	Lbs.	Doz.
W4659/6623 7½ oz. cup (009290)	3	16	$1.35
W4649 5¾″ saucer (009282)	3	14	1.05
W4638/71 7⅜″ salad plate (009233)	3	23	2.75
W4646/71 10″ dinner plate (009266)	3	44	3.75
W4647/71 12 x 9″ platter (009274)	1	20	6.00
W4678/71 8¼″ vegetable bowl (009324)	1	14	3.75
W4667/71 6⅝″ soup plate (009308)	3	25	2.75
W4674/71 4⅝″ dessert (009316)	3	11	1.35
W4643/6623 sugar/cover (009241)	1	9	3.00
W4644/6623 creamer (009258)	1	7	2.25

PACKED SETS

	Sets	Lbs.	Set
W4600/73 16 pc. set in gift display carton. Set contains four each cups, saucers, desserts and dinner plates. (009191)	4	38	2.75
W4600/74 35 pc. set. Set contains six each cups, saucers, desserts, soup plates and dinner plates. One each vegetable bowl, platter, sugar/ cover and creamer. (009209)	1	23	6.75
W4600/75 53 pc. set. Set contains eight each cups, saucers, desserts, salad plates, soup plates and dinner plates. One each vegetable bowl, platter, sugar/cover and creamer. (009217)	1	34	9.90

SORENO TABLE SERVICE SET

T4000/209 7 pc. Avocado table service set in gift display box. Set contains one salt shaker, one pepper shaker, one sugar and cover, one creamer, one butter and cover. (020321)	6	26	1.60

BULK PACKED

	Doz.	Lbs.	Doz.
T4053 sugar and cover (020289)	2	16	2.40
T4054 creamer (020297)	2	14	1.50
T4023 butter and cover (020305)	1	11	2.90
	Sets	Lbs.	Set
T4030-D salt and pepper shaker set (018267)	12	10	.60

SORENO LUNCHEON SETS

T4000/245 16 pc. Avocado set in a die-cut corrugated carton with a shrink film overwrap with plastic carrying handle. Set contains four each 7 oz. cups, 10″ plates, 5¾″ saucers and 5⅞″ bowls. (023457)	4	49	2.50
T4000/141 16 pc. Avocado set in gift display carton. Set contains four each 10″ plates, 7 oz. cups, 5¾″ saucers, 5⅞″ salad or soup bowls. (015743)	4	45	2.25

BULK PACKED

	Doz.	Lbs.	Doz.
T4079 7 oz. cup (013953)	3	16	1.20
T4041 10″ plate (013987)	3	38	2.40
T4029 5¾″ saucer (013961)	3	16	1.20
T4066 5⅞″ bowl (013979)	3	23	1.45

BLUE MOSAIC

W4638/71

W4674/71

W4646/71

W4659/6623 · W4649

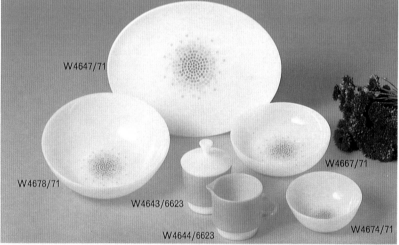

W4647/71

W4678/71

W4643/6623

W4644/6623

W4667/71

W4674/71

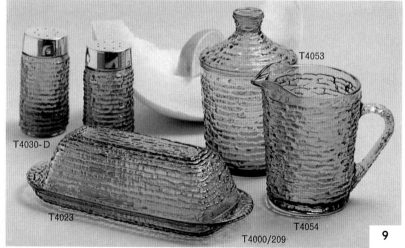

T4030-D

T4053

T4023

T4000/209

T4054

"BUBBLE"
(1930's-1960's)

COLORS: Sapphire Blue/B1600, Royal Ruby/R1600, Crystal/1600, Forest Green/E1600, Milk White/W1600, Pink/P1600, Topaz/T1600.

Some pieces of "Bubble" can be found in almost every color that Anchor Hocking made. However, the tableware sets came in only sapphire blue, crystal, forest green, milk white and royal ruby. There has been found a dinner plate, and a cup and saucer in pink. However, we have not come across any catalog listings for this color. The Sapphire Blue and the Crystal tableware sets have blue and silver labels that reads, FIRE-KING TABLE WARE, guaranteed heat proof.

"Bubble" got its start in the early 30's with some novelty items in sapphire blue that went by the names, "Provincial" and "Bullseye". The "Bubble" pattern was in production longer than any other pattern made by Anchor Hocking. The 8 ½" fancy bowl is one of the more common pieces. It's found in colors of jade-ite, milk white, pink, lustre, topaz as well as tableware colors.

The hard to find pieces are; in sapphire, sugar, 4" berry bowl, 9½" grill plate and the 9" flanged bowl; in pink everything except the 8¼" berry bowl; in royal ruby, 64 oz. pitcher; in forest green, 7" cereal bowl; in crystal, the candlesticks.

PRICE GUIDE

DESCRIPTION		-CRYSTAL	-F/GRN.	-R/RUBY	-SAPH/BLUE	MILK WHITE (CURRENT PRICES)
CUP	- 8 oz.	— $3.00	— $4.00	— $4.50	— $3.00	— $3.00
SAUCER	- 5 ¾"	— 1.00	— 2.00	— 2.50	— 2.00	— 2.00
PLATE, PIE OR SALAD	- 6 ¾"	— 2.00	— 3.50	— 4.00	— 3.00	— 3.00
PLATE, DINNER	- 9 ¼"	— 4.00	— 11.00	— 7.00	— 6.00	— 6.00
PLATE, GRILL	- 9 ¼"	—	—	—	— 15.00	—
PLATTER, OVAL	- 9"x12"	—	—	—	— 12.00	—
BOWL, BERRY	- 4"	— 3.00	—	—	— 11.00	— 4.00
BOWL, FRUIT	- 4 ½"	— 4.00	— 7.00	— 8.00	— 8.00	— 3.50
BOWL, FANCY*	- 8½"	— 8.00	—	—	— 12.00	— 7.00
BOWL, CEREAL	- 5 ¼"	— 5.00	—	—	— 9.00	— 5.00
BOWL, SOUP	- 7 ¾"	— 5.50	— 9.00	—	— 10.00	—
BOWL, VEGETABLE	- 8 ¼"	—	—	—	— 12.00	—
BOWL, FLANGED	- 9"	—	—	—	— 75.00	—
SUGAR, FOOTED, OPEN	-	— 5.00	— 8.00	—	— 14.00	— 4.00
CREAMER, FOOTED	-	— 5.00	— 9.00	—	— 28.00	— 4.00
TUMBLER, JUICE	- 6 oz.	— 4.00	—	— 6.00	—	—
TUMBLER, WATER	- 9 oz.	— 4.00	—	— 7.00	—	—
TUMBLER, ICED TEA	- 12 oz.	— 7.00	—	— 8.00	—	—
TUMBLER, LEMONADE	- 16 oz.	— 8.00	—	— 15.00	—	—
PITCHER, ICE LIP	- 64 oz.	— 60.00	—	— 45.00	—	—
CANDLESTICKS, PR.	-	— 14.00	- 25.00	—	—	—

*(Pink-8.00, Jade-ite-10.00, Peach Lustre-9.00)

MILK WHITE Anchorglass®

W1664   W1678   W1653 — W1654   W11

			PACKING
W1664—4½"	Dessert		6 doz. — 26 lbs.
W1678—8"	Bowl		1 doz. — 17 lbs.
W1653—	Sugar		2 doz. — 12 lbs.
W1654—	Creamer		2 doz. — 13 lbs.
W11—7 x 6½"	Shell Dish		2 doz. — 17 lbs.

1959-1960 Anchor Hocking Catalog

39.

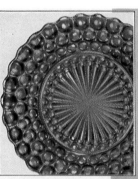

R1650 — R1628   R1664   R1641

R1650—	Cup		3 doz. — 12 lbs.
R1628—	Saucer		3 doz. — 13 lbs.
R1664—4½"	Dessert		3 doz. — 12 lbs.
R1641—9¼"	Dinner Plate		3 doz. — 43 lbs.

PREPACKED SETS

R1600/59—16 Pce. Luncheon Set
Each Set in Ptd. Parchment Box—
4 Sets in Shipping Carton — 39 lbs.
COMPOSITION:
Four R1650 Cups
Four R1628 Saucers
Four R1664 Desserts
Four R1641 Plates

R1600/60—20 Pce. Luncheon Set
Each Set in Ptd. Parchment Carton — 12 lbs.
COMPOSITION:
Four R1650 Cups
Four R1628 Saucers
Four R1664 Desserts
Four R1641 Plates
Four R1612 Tumblers

Ruby Tumblers to Match are shown on Page 35.

R1600/60

21.

12

1963 Anchor Hocking Catalog

CRYSTAL STEMWARE
ARTISTIC YET PRACTICAL

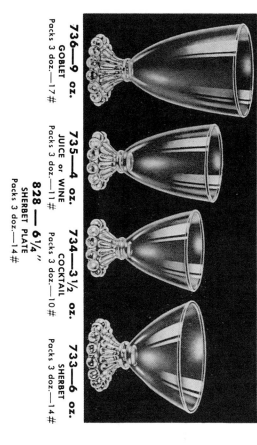

736 — 9 oz.
GOBLET
Packs 3 doz. — 17 #

735 — 4 oz.
JUICE or WINE
Packs 3 doz. — 11 #

734 — 3½ oz.
COCKTAIL
Packs 3 doz. — 10 #

733 — 6 oz.
SHERBET
Packs 3 doz. — 14 #

828 — 6¼"
SHERBET PLATE
Packs 3 doz. — 14 #

Sparkling, polished crystal; beautiful design. Lowest priced stemware on the market. Millions sold yearly.

EXQUISITE "EARLY AMERICAN" LINE

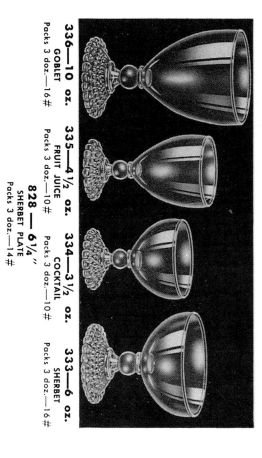

336 — 10 oz.
GOBLET
Packs 3 doz. — 16 #

335 — 4½ oz.
FRUIT JUICE
Packs 3 doz. — 10 #

334 — 3½ oz.
COCKTAIL
Packs 3 doz. — 10 #

333 — 6 oz.
SHERBET
Packs 3 doz. — 16 #

828 — 6¼"
SHERBET PLATE
Packs 3 doz. — 14 #

Charming and graceful. High quality, with that expensive look, yet priced for the masses.

CRYSTAL FIRE-KING DINNERWARE
DELIGHTFUL PARTY SERVICE

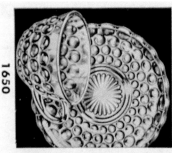

1650
CUP
Packs 6 doz. — 22 #

1628
SAUCER
Packs 6 doz. — 31 #

A delightful pattern with Early American charm. Sparkling polish gives brilliance and fine appearance. Very durable and economical—made from rugged FIRE-KING Heat-proof crystal glass.

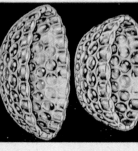

1664 — 4½"
DESSERT
Packs 6 doz. — 26 #

1665 — 5¼"
CEREAL
Packs 6 doz. — 35 #

1630 — 6⅝"
PIE OR SALAD PLATE
Packs 6 doz. — 37 #

1641 — 9¼"
DINNER PLATE
Packs 3 doz. — 39 #

PROMOTE SETS FOR GREATER PROFITS

20 PIECE LUNCH SET

Gift Packed

1600/33 — 20 Pce.
LUNCHEON SET

Each Set Pkd. in Gift Ctn., 4 Sets to R/S Ctn. — 46 #

COMPOSITION:
Four Cups
Four Saucers
Four Desserts
Four Salad Plates
Four Dinner Plates

20 PIECE LUNCH SET

Gift Packed

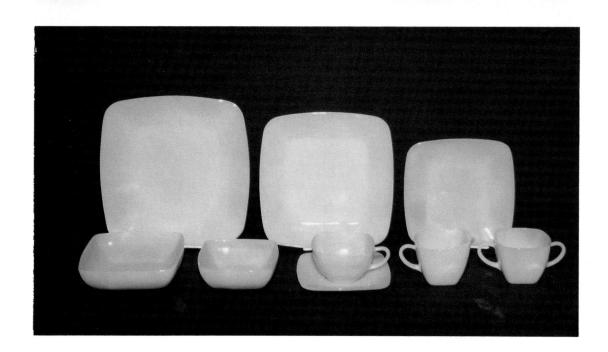

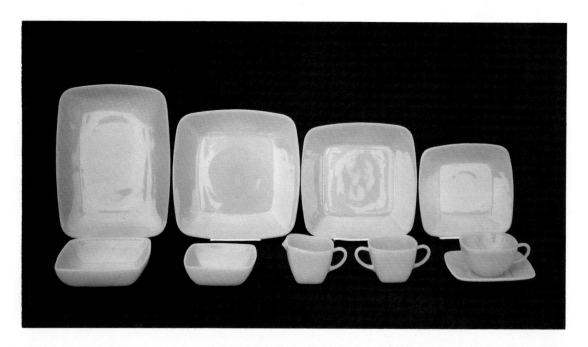

"CHARM (SQUARE) DINNERWARE"
(1950's)
(A2200/G2200)
(E2200/R2200)

COLORS: Azur-ite, Jade-ite, Forest Green, & Royal Ruby

Anchor Hocking made this pattern in several different colors, however only the colors of azur-ite and jade-ite inherited the "FIRE-KING" markings. Unlike most patterns of glassware which have a round shape, "Charm" was cast in a completely different square design.

When this pattern was packaged for sale, it wasn't always packed as a complete set. For instance, there was an ad for a sixteen piece luncheon set, consisting of four cups, four saucers, four cereals and four plates. If you desired the other size, of bowls and plates, you had to order them separately. Generally these items were never purchased, making them harder to find.

The majority of this pattern will not be embossed with the "FIRE-KING" trademark, but don't let that discourage you from collecting it. Embossed or not it is just as valuable. The pieces you do find marked will read (OVEN Fire-King GLASS).

PRICE GUIDE

DESCRIPTION		AZUR-ITE	JADE-ITE	FOREST GREEN	RUBY RED
CUP	- 8 oz.	— $3.00	— $3.00	— $4.00	— $4.50
SAUCER	- 5 3/8"	— 1.50	— 1.50	— 3.00	— 3.50
PLATE, DINNER	- 9 ¼"	— 6.00	— 7.00	— 9.00	— 10.00
PLATE, LUNCHEON	- 8 3/8"	— 5.00	— 6.00	— 8.00	— 9.00
PLATE, SALAD	- 6 5/8"	— 4.00	— 5.00	— 7.00	— 8.00
PLATTER	- 8"x11"	— 10.00	— 11.00	— 22.00	— 24.00
BOWL, DESSERT	- 4 ¾"	— 4.50	— 5.00	— 6.50	— 6.50
BOWL, SALAD	- 7 3/8"	— 5.00	— 5.50	— 8.00	— 10.00
BOWL, SOUP	- 6"	— 4.00	— 5.00	— 7.00	— 8.00
SUGAR	-	— 4.50	— 4.50	— 5.00	—
CREAMER	-	— 6.50	— 4.50	— 5.00	—

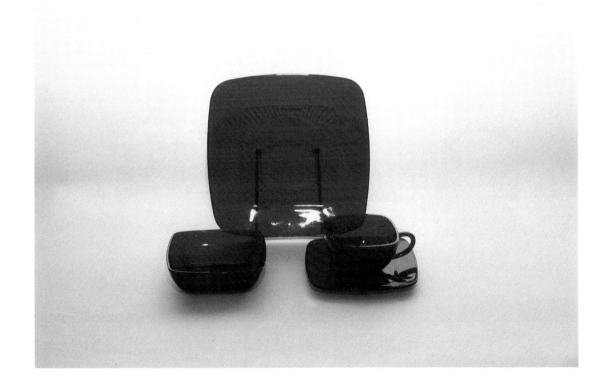

15

"FLEURETTE"
(1959-1960)
W4600

"Fleurette" was the first pattern of "FIRE-KING" to have a floral design applied to each piece. This pattern is easy to identify. It has a cluster of red flowers with yellow centers, brown with black edged leaves and brown stems. This design is applied to the center of the plates and bowls, on the sides of the cups, sugar and creamer, and on the inner rim of the saucers.

The hard to find pieces are as usual the bowls, specially the soup and vegetable. The bread and butter seems to be a little difficult to find. Also, as with any applied pattern of glassware, the design fades with use and time. Finding pieces in mint condition is going to take some time.

The "Fleurette" pattern offered a gift boxed snack set, that included 4 rectangular trays with cup indent in one corner and 4 small 5 oz. cups.

The trademark found on "Fleurette" is (OVEN Fire-King WARE MADE IN U.S.A.), some will have a mold number between the WARE and the MADE IN U.S.A.

PRICE GUIDE

DESCRIPTION		CURRENT PRICES	
CUP	- 8 oz.	—	$3.00
SAUCER	- 5 ¾"	—	1.00
PLATE, BREAD & BUTTER	- 6 ¼"	—	2.00
PLATE, SALAD	- 7 3/8"	—	3.00
PLATE, DINNER	- 9 1/8"	—	5.00
PLATTER	- 9"x12"	—	6.00
BOWL, DESSERT	- 4 5/8"	—	3.00
BOWL, SOUP	- 6 5/8"	—	5.00
BOWL, VEGETABLE	- 8 ¼"	—	6.00
SUGAR & LID*	-	—	4.00
CREAMER	-	—	3.00
PLATE, SNACK SET	- 6"x11"	—	3.00
CUP, SNACK SET	- 5 oz.	—	1.00

*Sugar without lid deduct $1.00.

~~~~~~

"GAME BIRDS"
(1959-1962)
W4600

The "Game Birds" series dinnerware features four different wildlife scenes, Mallard Duck, Canadian Goose, Ring-neck Pheasant and Ruffled Grouse. This dinnerware came as a four place setting in the Anchorwhite W4600 line and had several accessory pieces available. The "Game Birds" series like most all of the W4600 lines had a set of tumblers that matched. In this case the tumblers were made of anchorwhite glass instead of the usual clear glass with matching patterns. Among the accessory items were a set of 4 anchorwhite ashtrays with the "Game Birds" scenes.

The trademarks found on this set are (OVEN Fire-King WARE, mold #, MADE IN U.S.A.), and (ANCHOR HOCKING [anchor over H] Fire-King WARE, mold #, MADE IN U.S.A.).

The hard to find pieces are the glasses which are the only anchorwhite glasses of this type we have ever found. These glasses are not trademarked.

PRICE GUIDE

DESCRIPTION		CURRENT PRICES	
PLATE, BREAD & BUTTER	- 6 ¼"	—	$2.50
PLATE, SALAD	- 7 3/8"	—	3.00
PLATE, DINNER	- 9 1/8"	—	6.00
BOWL, DESSERT	- 4 5/8"	—	3.50
BOWL, SOUP	- 6 5/8"	—	5.00
BOWL, VEGETABLE	- 8 ¼"	—	10.00
SUGAR & LID*	-	—	6.00
CREAMER	-	—	5.00
BOWL, CHILI	- 5"	—	5.00
MUG	- 8 oz.	—	5.50
TUMBLER	- 11 oz.	—	5.50
ASHTRAYS	- 5 ¼"	—	4.50

*Sugar without lid deduct $1.00.

FLEURETTE® DINNERWARE

W4679/58 — W4629/58

W4674/58

W4637/58 — W4638/58 — W4641/58

PACKING

W4679/58—8 oz.	Cup	6 doz. — 25 lbs.
W4629/58—5 ¾"	Saucer	6 doz. — 27 lbs.
W4674/58—4 ⅝"	Dessert	6 doz. — 21 lbs.
W4637/58—6 ¼"	Bread & Butter Plate	3 doz. — 16 lbs.
W4638/58—7 ⅜"	Salad Plate	3 doz. — 23 lbs.
W4641/58—9 ⅛"	Dinner Plate	3 doz. — 39 lbs.

W4667/58

Fleurette
Prepacked Sets
are shown on
Page 3.

W4647/58

W4667/58— 6 ⅝"	Soup Plate	3 doz. — 27 lbs.
W4647/58—12 x 9"	Platter	1 doz. — 20 lbs.

W4678/58

See Prepacked
Serva-Snack Set
on Page 3.

W4653/58 — W4654/58

W4678/58—8 ¼"	Vegetable Bowl	1 doz. — 15 lbs.
W4653/58—	Sugar & Cover	2 doz. — 16 lbs.
W4654/58—	Creamer	2 doz. — 12 lbs.

HEAT-PROOF

2.

DECORATED MUGS AND BOWLS — HEAT-PROOF

W1212/5931 — W1212/5932 — W1212/5933 — W1212/5934

W291/5931 — W291/5932 — W291/5933 — W291/5934

	PACKING
W1212/5931—8 oz. Coffee Mug—"Ruffed Grouse" Dec.	4 doz. — 27 lbs.
W1212/5932—8 oz. Coffee Mug—"Ring-Necked Pheasant" Dec.	4 doz. — 27 lbs.
W1212/5933—8 oz. Coffee Mug—"Canada Goose" Dec.	4 doz. — 27 lbs.
W1212/5934—8 oz. Coffee Mug—"Mallard Duck" Dec.	4 doz. — 27 lbs.
W291/5931—5" Soup or Cereal—"Ruffed Grouse" Dec.	4 doz. — 29 lbs.
W291/5932—5" Soup or Cereal—"Ring-Necked Pheasant" Dec.	4 doz. — 29 lbs.
W291/5933—5" Soup or Cereal—"Canada Goose" Dec.	4 doz. — 29 lbs.
W291/5934—5" Soup or Cereal—"Mallard Duck" Dec.	4 doz. — 29 lbs.

MILK WHITE ASH TRAYS

W142/5931 — W142/5932 — W142/5933 — W142/5934

WILD BIRD DECORATIONS

W142/5931—5 ¼ "—"Ruffed Grouse" Dec.	2 doz. — 17 lbs.
W142/5932—5 ¼ "—"Ringed-Necked Pheasant" Dec.	2 doz. — 17 lbs.
W142/5933—5 ¼ "—"Canada Goose" Dec.	2 doz. — 17 lbs.
W142/5934—5 ¼ "—"Mallard Duck" Dec.	2 doz. — 17 lbs.

"GOLDEN ANNIVERSARY" 50TH, YEAR
(1955-1958)
W4100/50
22K IVORY DINNERWARE

To celebrate the 50th year of producing some of the most beautiful, yet affordable, glassware in America, Anchor Hocking Glass Corp. introduced the "Golden Anniversary" dinnerware in an Ivory Swirl pattern, heavily trimmed in 22K gold. This pattern easily became one of the most elegant dinnerware sets to carry the "FIRE-KING" trademark.

The hard to find pieces are, the large bowls, with the vegetable bowl being the hardest, the oval platter, and for some reason the cups.

The trademark found on this pattern is, (OVEN Fire-King WARE MADE IN THE U.S.A.).

There is a lot of confusion between the "Golden Anniversary" and the "22K Gold" patterns. Here are two ways to help you distinguish between them. One, the "Golden Anniversary" is ivory in color and the "22K Gold" is white. Yes, we agree that in poor light they do look a lot alike. Two, the "Golden Anniversary" has a wider band of gold trim than the "22K Gold."

PRICE GUIDE

DESCRIPTION		CURRENT PRICES
CUP	- 8 oz.	— $3.00
SAUCER	- 5 ¾"	— 1.00
PLATE, SALAD	- 7 ¾"	— 4.00
PLATE, DINNER	- 9 1/8"	— 6.00
PLATTER, OVAL	- 9"x 12"	— 10.00
BOWL, DESSERT	- 4 7/8"	— 3.50
BOWL, SOUP	- 7 5/8"	— 5.00
BOWL, VEGETABLE	- 8 ¼"	— 10.00
SUGAR, OPEN	-	— 5.00
CREAMER	-	— 5.00

~~~~~~

"22K GOLD"
(1959-1962)
W4100

The "22k gold" tableware set is without a doubt the most commonly found pattern of "FIRE-KING". In the catalog listings of this pattern Anchor Hocking referred to it as "Golden Anniversary" anchorwhite. It is easily recognized by it's 22k gold trimmed edge on the anchorwhite swirl (W4100) line of tableware. By the way, that's real 22k gold so don't use in the microwave or you may get a plain white swirl piece minus the gold.

There are no hard to find pieces for now. But, finding this pattern in mint condition might be a little tough. If it was used a lot the gold trim tended to wear. This was the first set of "FIRE-KING" tableware we completed. And we have found a few pieces with the original labels that read, (HEAT-PROOF 22K-GOLD Anchorglass Anchor Hocking Glass Corp. Lancaster Ohio U.S.A.).

The trademark found on this pattern is, (OVEN Fire-King WARE MADE IN U.S.A.). The mold number located under the word "WARE" was used by Anchor Hocking to identify the mold, should a flaw be found in a piece of glass.

There are several white "Party Ware" pieces trimmed in 22k gold that go very well with this set. The egg plate and the round relish do not have the "FIRE-KING" trademark.

PRICE GUIDE

DESCRIPTION		CURRENT PRICES
CUP	- 8 oz.	— $3.00
SAUCER	- 5 ¾"	— 1.00
PLATE, SALAD	- 7 ¾"	— 4.00
PLATE, DINNER	- 9 1/8"	— 6.00
PLATTER, OVAL	- 9" x 12"	— 10.00
BOWL, DESSERT	- 4 7/8"	— 3.50
BOWL, SOUP	- 7 5/8"	— 5.00
BOWL, VEGETABLE	- 8 ¼"	— 10.00
SUGAR, OPEN	-	— 5.00
CREAMER	-	— 5.00

Golden Anniversary Egg Plate & Golden Veil Snack Set

"GOLDEN ANNIVERSARY" 50TH, YEAR

DESCRIPTION	PRICE GUIDE CURRENT PRICES
PARTY WARE	
EGG PLATE	— $7.50
RELISH, OVAL (3 Part)	— 7.50
RELISH, ROUND (3 Part)	— 7.50

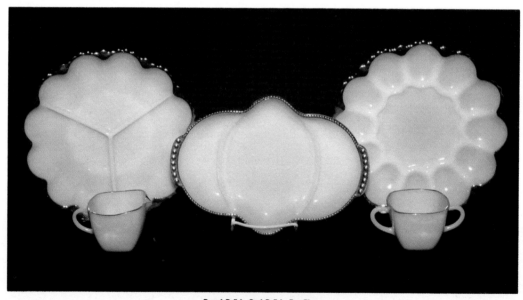

Round Relish, Oval Relish, Egg Plate.
Square Creamer, Square Sugar.

"22K GOLD"

DESCRIPTION	PRICE GUIDE CURRENT PRICES
PARTY WARE	
EGG PLATE	— $6.00
RELISH, OVAL (3 Part)	— 6.00
RELISH, ROUND (3 Part)	— 6.00

Box Illustration

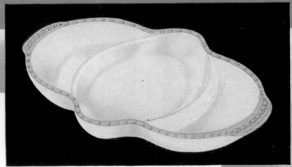

W50-G/13

PACKING

W50-G/13—11⅛" Divided Relish .... 1 doz. — 24 lbs.

Each Divided Relish is packed in an Individual Display Box as illustrated.

W896-G/13

W898-G/13

W896-G/13—9¾" Egg Plate .... 1 doz. — 22 lbs.
W898-G/13—9¾" Divided Dish .... 1 doz. — 24 lbs.

The Above Items are in Individual Display Box as illustrated.

"VINTAGE" DESIGN

W657-G/13

W658-G/13

W657-G/13—8½" Ftd. Bowl—Vintage Design .... 1 doz. — 24 lbs.
W658-G/13—9" Deep Bowl—Vintage Design .... 1 doz. — 26 lbs.

**All Items on this page are packed in Individual Display Boxes as illustrated,
then 12 Boxes to a Shipping Carton. Not Assorted.**

59.

GOLDEN ANNIVERSARY DINNERWARE

W4179/50 — W4129/50   W4174/50   W4138/50 — W4141/50   W4167/50

		PACKING	
W4179/50—	Cup	6 doz. — 26 lbs.
W4129/50—	Saucer	6 doz. — 28 lbs.
W4174/50—4 ⅞"	Dessert	6 doz. — 24 lbs.
W4138/50—7 ¾"	Salad Plate	3 doz. — 26 lbs.
W4141/50—9 ⅛"	Dinner Plate	3 doz. — 38 lbs.
W4167/50—7 ⅝"	Soup Plate	3 doz. — 29 lbs.

IVORY-WHITE GLASS WITH 22 K. GOLD TRIM.   **HEAT-PROOF**

W4178/50   W4147/50   W4153/50 — W4154/50

W4178/50— 8 ¼"	Vegetable Bowl	1 doz. — 15 lbs.
W4147/50—12 x 9"	Platter	1 doz. — 21 lbs.
W4153/50—	Sugar	2 doz. — 10 lbs.
W4154/50—	Creamer	2 doz. — 10 lbs.

W4100/57

PREPACKED SETS

W4100/57—18 Pce. Luncheon Set

Each Set in Gift Carton, 4 Sets to Shipping Carton — 41 lbs.

COMPOSITION:

Four W4179/50 Cups	Four W4141/50 Dinner Plates
Four W4129/50 Saucers	One W4153/50 Sugar
Four W4174/50 Desserts	One W4154/50 Creamer

W4100/58—34 Pce. Dinner Set

Each Set in Shipping Carton — 23 lbs.

COMPOSITION:

Six W4179/50 Cups	One W4178/50 Vegetable Bowl
Six W4129/50 Saucers	One W4147/50 Platter
Six W4174/50 Desserts	One W4153/50 Sugar
Six W4138/50 Salad Plates	One W4154/50 Creamer
Six W4141/50 Dinner Plates	

W4100/59—52 Pce. Dinner Set

Each Set in Shipping Carton — 35 lbs.

COMPOSITION:

Eight W4179/50 Cups	Eight W4141/50 Dinner Plates
Eight W4129/50 Saucers	One W4178/50 Vegetable Bowl
Eight W4174/50 Desserts	One W4147/50 Platter
Eight W4138/50 Salad Plates	One W4153/50 Sugar
Eight W4167/50 Soup Plates	One W4154/50 Creamer

19.

GOLDEN ANNIVERSARY DINNERWARE

W4100/57—18 Pce. Luncheon Set
Each Set in Gift Carton, 4 Sets to Shipping Carton — 41 lbs.
COMPOSITION:
Four W4179/50 Cups   Four W4141/50 Dinner Plates
Four W4129/50 Saucers   One W4153/50 Sugar
Four W4174/50 Desserts   One W4154/50 Creamer

W4100/58—34 Pce. Dinner Set (Not illustrated)
Each Set in Shipping Carton — 23 lbs.
COMPOSITION:
Six W4179/50 Cups   One W4178/50 Vegetable Bowl
Six W4129/50 Saucers   One W4147/50 Platter
Six W4174/50 Desserts   One W4153/50 Sugar
Six W4138/50 Salad Plates   One W4154/50 Creamer
Six W4141/50 Dinner Plates

W4100/59—52 Pce. Dinner Set (Not illustrated)
Each Set in Shipping Carton — 35 lbs.
COMPOSITION:
Eight W4179/50 Cups   Eight W4141/50 Dinner Plates
Eight W4129/50 Saucers   One W4178/50 Vegetable Bowl
Eight W4174/50 Desserts   One W4147/50 Platter
Eight W4138/50 Salad Plates   One W4153/50 Sugar
Eight W4167/50 Soup Plates   One W4154/50 Creamer

W4100/57

OPEN STOCK

W4179/50 — W4129/50

W4174/50

W4138/50 — W4141/50

W4167/50

		PACKING
W4179/50—	Cup	6 doz. — 26 lbs.
W4129/50—	Saucer	6 doz. — 28 lbs.
W4174/50—4 7/8"	Dessert	6 doz. — 24 lbs.
W4138/50—7 3/4"	Salad Plate	3 doz. — 26 lbs.
W4141/50—9 1/8"	Dinner Plate	3 doz. — 40 lbs.
W4167/50—7 5/8"	Soup Plate	3 doz. — 29 lbs.

W4178/50

W4147/50

W4153/50 — W4154/50

W4178/50— 8 1/4"	Vegetable Bowl	1 doz. — 15 lbs.
W4147/50—12 x 9"	Platter	1 doz. — 21 lbs.
W4153/50—	Sugar	2 doz. — 10 lbs.
W4154/50—	Creamer	2 doz. — 10 lbs.

HEAT-PROOF   **ANCHORWHITE — 22 K. GOLD TRIMMED**

4,

"HARVEST"
(1968-1971)
W4600/77

"Harvest" is one of the more elegant patterns of the W4600 line of dinnerware. It is white with light and dark gray grain sheaths which form a circle in the center of the plates. The cups are of the stacking style first used in the "Blue Mosaic" tableware and are white with two sheaths, one on each side.

As for hard to find pieces, very little of this pattern is showing up in the flea markets, antique malls, or glassware shows. The only pieces we have been able to locate turned up in a thrift store in Ohio.

The trademarks found on this pattern are, (ANCHOR HOCKING [anchor over H symbol] Fire-King WARE, mold #, MADE IN U.S.A.), and (ANCHOR HOCKING [anchor over H symbol] Fire-King WARE, mold #, MADE IN U.S.A.), and (ANCHOR HOCKING [anchor over H symbol] Fire-King DINNERWARE, mold #, MADE IN U.S.A.).

PRICE GUIDE

DESCRIPTION		CURRENT PRICES
CUP, STACKING	- 7 ½ oz.	— $2.00
SAUCER	- 5 ¾"	— 1.00
PLATE, SALAD	- 7 3/8"	— 3.00
PLATE, DINNER	- 10"	— 4.00
PLATTER, OVAL	- 9"x 12"	— 5.00
BOWL, DESSERT	- 4 5/8"	— 3.00
BOWL, SOUP	- 6 5/8"	— 5.00
BOWL, VEGETABLE	- 8 ¼"	— 6.00
SUGAR, LID*	-	— 4.00
CREAMER	-	— 4.00

*Sugar without lid deduct $1.00.

W4678/77

W4647/77

W4643/77

W4644/77

W4638/77

W4667/77

W4674/77

W4646/77

W4659/77
W4649/77

HARVEST	CARTON	
(heat resistant)	Doz.	Lbs.
W4659/77 7½ oz. stacking cup (086538)	3	16
W4649/77 5¾″ saucer (086546)	3	14
W4674/77 4⅝″ dessert (086553)	3	11
W4667/77 6⅝″ soup or salad bowl (086587)	3	23
W4638/77 7⅜″ salad plate (086561)	3	21
W4646/77 10″ dinner plate (086579)	3	44
W4678/77 8¼″ vegetable bowl (086595)	1	14
W4647/77 12x9″ platter (086603)	1	20
W4643/77 sugar/cover (086611)	1	9
W4644/77 creamer (086629)	1	7

PACKED SETS	CARTON	
	Sets	Lbs.
W4600/81 16 pc. set in display ctn. with shrink-film wrap and carry-out handle. Set contains four cups, saucers, soup or salad bowls and dinner plates. (086637)	4	47
W4600/82 45 pc. set in shipping ctn. with full color litho label. Set contains eight cups, saucers, desserts, soup or salad bowls and dinner plates. One vegetable bowl, platter, sugar/cover and creamer. (086645)	1	31

"This ad really communicates:
dinnerware so translucent
I can see my hand through it—
but it's ovenware sturdy."

We married the beauty of fine china to the strength of ovenware.

Anchor Hocking's new "dimension" dinnerware... superb table settings you can use every day.
You can see your hand through it (just like fine china), yet it takes abuse like the toughest ovenware.
And it costs less than $2 for a 6 piece open-stock setting.

3 other "dimension" patterns...

ANCHOR HOCKING

W4678/76

W4647/76

W4643/6770

W4644/6770

W4638/76

W4667/76

W4674/76

W4646/76

W4659/6770
W4649

HOMESTEAD	CARTON	
(heat resistant)	Doz.	Lbs.
W4659/6770 7½ oz. stacking cup (086744)	3	16
W4649 5¾" plain saucer (009282)	3	14
W4674/76 4⅝" dessert (086751)	3	11
W4667/76 6⅝" soup or salad bowl (086785)	3	23
W4638/76 7⅜" salad plate (086769)	3	21
W4646/76 10" dinner plate (086777)	3	44
W4678/76 8¼" vegetable bowl (086793)	1	14
W4647/76 12x9" platter (086801)	1	20
W4643/6770 sugar/cover (086819)	1	9
W4644/6770 creamer (086827)	1	7

PACKED SETS	CARTON	
	Sets	Lbs.
W4600/83 16 pc. set in gift display ctn. with shrink-film wrap and carry-out handle. Set contains four cups, saucers, soup or salad bowls and dinner plates. (086835)	4	47
W4600/84 45 pc. set in shipping ctn. with full color litho label. Set contains eight cups, saucers, desserts, soup or salad bowl and dinner plates. One vegetable bowl, platter, creamer and sugar/cover. (086843)	1	31

"HOMESTEAD"
(1968-1970)
W4600/76

"Homestead" is the third issue of the W4600 line of dinnerware and is white with a red, black, and gray scroll design in the center of the plates. It has stacking cups and a handleless sugar with lid which are traits of the 4600 line of the late 60's.

The hard to find pieces are, everything! We have not been able to locate a single piece of this set. But we do have some very nice color copies of the Anchor Hocking sales catalog from 1968.

As for trademarks, they are, (ANCHOR HOCKING [anchor over H symbol] Fire-King, mold #, WARE MADE IN U.S.A.), and (ANCHOR HOCKING [anchor over H symbol] Fire-King DINNERWARE, mold # MADE IN U.S.A.).

PRICE GUIDE

DESCRIPTION		CURRENT PRICES
CUP, STACKING	- 7 ½ oz.	— $2.00
SAUCER	- 5 ¾"	— 1.00
PLATE, SALAD	- 7 3/8"	— 3.00
PLATE, DINNER	- 10"	— 4.00
PLATTER, OVAL	- 9"x 12"	— 5.00
BOWL, DESSERT	- 4 5/8"	— 3.00
BOWL, SOUP	- 6 5/8"	— 5.00
BOWL, VEGETABLE	- 8 ¼"	— 6.00
SUGAR, LID*	-	— 4.00
CREAMER	-	— 4.00

*Sugar without lid deduct $1.00.

"HONEYSUCKLE"
(1959-1962)
W4600

The "Honeysuckle" pattern is another example of the late 1950's floral design dinnerware sets. It can be identified by red flowers, dark green and brown leaves with brown stemmed clusters on this W4600 anchorwhite glassware. The floral design is located in the center of the plates and bowls, also on the sides of the cups, sugar and creamer. The saucers have the design on the inner rim.

The trademark found on this pattern is (OVEN Fire-King WARE MADE IN U.S.A.), with a mold number between WARE and MADE IN U.S.A.

The hard to find pieces are 6 3/16" bread and butter, 4 5/8" dessert, and 8¼" vegetable bowl. We haven't been able to locate the sugar and creamer. There should be a snack set but it has eluded us as well. So there's still some fun left in collecting this pattern.

PRICE GUIDE

DESCRIPTION		CURRENT PRICES
CUP	- 8 oz.	— $3.00
SAUCER	- 5¾"	— 1.00
PLATE, BREAD & BUTTER	- 6¼"	— 2.00
PLATE, SALAD	- 7 3/8"	— 3.00
PLATE, DINNER	- 9 1/8"	— 5.00
PLATTER, OVAL	- 9" x 12"	— 6.00
BOWL, DESSERT	- 4 5/8"	— 3.00
BOWL, SOUP	- 6 5/8"	— 6.00
BOWL, VEGETABLE	- 8¼"	— 6.00
SUGAR & LID*	-	— 4.00
CREAMER	-	— 3.00
PLATE, SNACK SET	- 6" x 11"	— 3.00
CUP, SNACK SET	- 5 oz.	— 1.00

*Sugar without lid deduct $1.00.

Honeysuckle Dinnerware

★ OVEN - PROOF!

★ EASY TO CLEAN!

★ DISHWASHER SAFE!

★ PERMANENT DECORATION!

COMPLETE 53-PC. SERVICE FOR EIGHT!

Honeysuckle DECORATED Glasses

★ 8 JUICE GLASSES

★ 8 WATER GLASSES

★ 8 ICED TEAS

COMPLETE 24-PC. SERVICE FOR EIGHT!

PR-7
4-59

"IVORY"
(1945-1957)
W1700

This is one of the oldest tableware sets to carry the "FIRE-KING" trademark. It was made using the 1700 line molds, the same molds were used to make "Royal Ruby" tableware of the early 1940's. It has a flat smooth look with no design molded to any of the pieces. We have found very little information on this set, in the way of catalog listings or magazine ads. But by comparing the pieces we have, to the "Royal Ruby" pieces, this set of tableware can be safely dated from mid 1940's to the mid 1950's.

The trademarks are, (OVEN Fire-King GLASS), (OVEN Fire-King WARE) and (OVEN Fire-King WARE MADE IN U.S.A.), with most of the cups not having a trademark.

There are two other cups that go well with this set, one being the "St. Denis" (a large 9 oz. cup with a very small finger ring) and the other being the "Ransom" 9 oz. cup (with a large sharp pointed finger ring). Both using the same unique saucer, having a deep rolled rim style. The labels read, (IVORY heat-proof Fire-King Anchor Hocking Corp. Lancaster, Ohio U.S.A.).

	PRICE GUIDE	
DESCRIPTION		CURRENT PRICES
CUP	- 8 oz.	— $3.00
SAUCER	- 5 ¾"	— 2.00
PLATE, SALAD	- 7 ¾"	— 3.00
PLATE, DINNER	- 9 1/8"	— 6.00
PLATTER, OVAL	- 9"x 12"	— 8.00
BOWL, FRUIT	- 4 ¼"	— 4.00
BOWL, SOUP	- 7 ½"	— 5.00
BOWL, VEGETABLE	- 8 ½"	— 10.00
SUGAR, OPEN	-	— 5.00
CREAMER	-	— 5.00
MUG	- 8 oz.	— 3.50
BOWL, CHILI	- 5"	— 3.00
CUP, ST. DENIS	- 9 oz.	— 4.00
CUP, RANSOM	- 9 oz.	— 4.00
SAUCER, DEEP	- 5 ¾"	— 2.00

IVORY *Fire-King* HEAT-PROOF ITEMS

★ W291   ★ W1212   ★ W384 — ★ W327   ★ W383 — ★ W327

			COST DOZ.	PACKING
★ W291—5"	Soup or Cereal		.62	4 doz. — 32 lbs.
★ W1212—8 oz.	Coffee Mug		.62	4 doz. — 31 lbs.
★ W384—9 oz.	St. Denis Cup		.54	4 doz. — 22 lbs.
★ W383—8 oz.	Ransom Cup		.48	4 doz. — 22 lbs.
★ W327—5⅞"	Saucer		.48	4 doz. — 21 lbs.
W341—9⅛"	Plate		1.25	3 doz. — 41 lbs.

(Illustrated Below)

Listed Above ←

W341

RANGE SET ↓

MIXING BOWLS

★ W355 — ★ W356 — ★ W357 — ★ W300/130

★ W23S   ★ W24   ★ W23P

★ W23S—4¼"	Salt Shaker—Litho Top		.65	4 doz. — 17 lbs.
★ W23P—4¼"	Pepper Shaker—Litho Top		.65	4 doz. — 17 lbs.
★ W24—16 oz.	Canister—Litho Top		.95	4 doz. — 32 lbs.
★ W355—4⅞"	Mixing Bowl		.64	3 doz. — 19 lbs.
★ W356—6"	Mixing Bowl		.95	3 doz. — 34 lbs.
★ W357—7¼"	Mixing Bowl		1.55	3 doz. — 56 lbs.
★ W300/130—3 Pce.	Mixing Bowl Set		3.14 doz.	3 doz. —109 lbs.
	(Bulk Packed in 3 ctns.)		sets	sets
	COMP.: One each W355, W356 and W357 Bowls.			

*Reg. U. S. Pat. Off.

PRINTED IN U.S.A.

Listing with ANCHOR HOCKING GLASS CORP., Lancaster, Ohio, U. S. A.   25.

"JADE-ITE BREAKFAST SET"
(1954-1956)
G300/186

The breakfast set is one of the most unique sets of "FIRE-KING" made in the jade-ite color. It consists of three common open stock pieces, the St. Denis cup and saucer, and the double egg cup. Three pieces unique to this set are the 20 oz. milk pitcher, 16 oz. 5" bowl, and the 9 1/8" plate. The 16 oz. 5" bowl is quite different from the standard 5" cereal bowl. It is about 1/4" taller, is thinner cast, and has a wider, flatter bottom. The plate (though very similar to the restaurant plate) is cast much thinner and does not have the rolled bead edge of the restaurant plate.

The hard to find pieces are, the 16 oz. 5" bowl and the 9 1/8" plate. Also the egg cups are getting harder to find.

The trademarks on this set are, (OVEN Fire-King GLASS), (OVEN Fire-King WARE), and (OVEN Fire-King WARE MADE IN U.S.A.). The egg cups are not marked.

We found our first complete breakfast set in a small country antique shop about 20 miles from where we live. The lady who sold it to the shop bought it still in the box with the labels on each piece. It was dusty so she washed it, and threw away the box and the labels.

PRICE GUIDE

DESCRIPTION		CURRENT PRICES
CUP (St. Denis)	- 9 oz.	— $5.00
SAUCER	- 5 7/8"	— 2.00
PLATE	- 9 1/8"	— 8.00
BOWL, CEREAL	- 16 oz., 5"	— 10.00
DOUBLE EGG CUP	-	— 10.00
PITCHER, MILK	- 20 oz.	— 20.00

21 PIECE JADE-ITE BREAKFAST SET: Four each-cups, saucers, cereal bowls, plates and double egg cups. One milk pitcher
....$155.00

"JADE-ITE RESTAURANT WARE"
(1948-1974)
G200-G300

Production of "Jade-ite Restaurant-Ware" began in the late 1940's. It quickly became one of Anchor Hocking's top selling, and longest running lines of all time. Due, without a doubt, to the durability of the heat-proof formula glass by the name of "FIRE-KING", and the versatile beauty of it's jade-ite color. With a cost of just pennies for each piece, no wonder it was so popular.

The best way to identify restaurant-ware is by its extra heavy construction, almost twice as thick as all other patterns of "FIRE-KING" tableware.

The trademarks on this pattern are, (FIRE-KING OVEN GLASS), (OVEN Fire-King GLASS), (OVEN Fire-King WARE), (OVEN Fire-King WARE MADE IN U.S.A.), and (ANCHOR HOCKING OVEN Fire-King WARE MADE IN U.S.A.). Due to its very long production run you will find almost every trademark Anchor Hocking ever used.

As for hard to find items, there shouldn't be any problem finding any of this glassware. But we have only been able to locate one 9 ¾" oval sandwich plate. Due to the heavy use of most of the pieces, it is pretty tough to find in mint condition.

PRICE GUIDE

DESCRIPTION		CURRENT PRICES	DESCRIPTION		CURRENT PRICES
CUP, STRAIGHT	- 8 oz.	— $3.50	BOWL, FLANGED	- 9"	— $16.00
CUP, EXTRA HEAVY	- 7 oz.	— 4.00	PLATE, BREAD & BUTTER	- 5 ½"	— 4.00
CUP, NARROW RIM	- 7 oz.	— 4.00	PLATE, PIE OR SALAD	- 6 ¾"	— 4.00
SAUCER	- 6"	— 2.00	PLATE, LUNCHEON	- 8"	— 6.00
MUG, EXTRA HEAVY	- 7 oz.	— 4.00	PLATE, DINNER	- 9"	— 7.00
MUG, SLIM*	- 6 oz.	— 4.00	PLATE, 3-COMPARTMENT	- 9 5/8"	— 10.00
BOWL, FRUIT	- 4 5/8"	— 3.50	PLATE, 5-COMPARTMENT	- 9 5/8"	— 10.00
BOWL, CEREAL	- 6¼"; 8 oz.	— 6.00	PLATE, OVAL SANDWICH	- 9 ¾"	— 12.00
BOWL	- 6 ¼"; 10 oz.	— 7.00	PLATE, OVAL	- 9 ½"	— 10.00
BOWL	- 5 5/8"; 15 oz.	— 8.00	PLATE, OVAL	- 11 ½"	— 12.00

*The slim mug is made for the 5-compartment plate.

JADE-ITE HEAVY DUTY RESTAURANT WARE

Cuts Your Dinnerware Costs in Half!

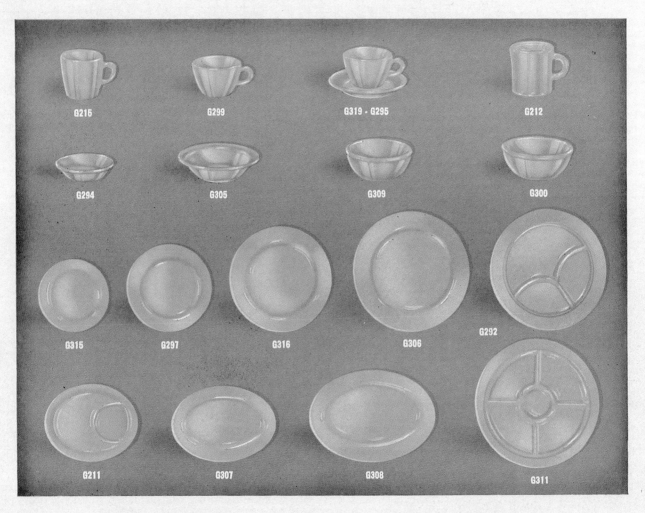

	COST DOZ.	PACKING
G215— 6 oz. Cup	.91	4 doz. — 35 lbs.
G299— 7 oz. Cup—Extra Heavy	.91	4 doz. — 36 lbs.
G319— 7 oz. Cup	.91	4 doz. — 34 lbs.
G295— 6" Saucer	.80	4 doz. — 31 lbs.
G212— 7 oz. Coffee Mug—Extra Heavy	1.61	4 doz. — 48 lbs.
G294— 4¾" Fruit	.54	6 doz. — 30 lbs.
G305— 8 oz. Cereal	.91	4 doz. — 37 lbs.
G309—10 oz. Bowl	.80	4 doz. — 30 lbs.
G300—15 oz. Bowl	1.18	4 doz. — 43 lbs.
G315— 5½" Bread & Butter	.75	4 doz. — 26 lbs.
G297— 6¾" Pie or Salad Plate	.86	4 doz. — 35 lbs.
G316— 8" Luncheon Plate	1.18	2 doz. — 30 lbs.
G306— 9" Dinner Plate	1.77	2 doz. — 33 lbs.
G292— 9⅝" 3-Compartment Plate	1.98	2 doz. — 38 lbs.
G211—Although illustrated cannot be supplied		
G307— 9½" Oval Platter	1.50	2 doz. — 24 lbs.
G308—11½" Oval Platter	2.30	1 doz. — 20 lbs.
G311—Although illustrated cannot be supplied		
G216— 9¾" Oval Sandwich Plate	1.77	2 doz. — 29 lbs.
(Not Illustrated)		

Listing with ANCHOR HOCKING GLASS CORP., Lancaster, Ohio, U. S. A.   37.

36   1953 Anchor Hocking Catalog

LUNCH COUNTER SERVICE
STURDY — HEAT-PROOF — LOW-PRICED
JADE-ITE RESTAURANT WARE

For your Lunch Counter Service, we highly recommend our Heavy Duty Jade-ite Restaurant ware. It is strong and sturdy, colorful and very low priced. You can make real savings thru its use. It is in service in many Chain Stores, Drug Stores, Restaurants and Hotels, as well as being used in some of the largest Industrial Cafeterias in America. Order a trial shipment with your next glassware order and let it prove itself. We would be glad to supply your Fountain needs too, as shown on next page.

G212 — 7 oz.
MUG — EXTRA HEAVY
Packs 4 doz.—48#

G319—7 oz. G295—6"
CUP   SAUCER
4 doz.—32# 4 doz.—31#

G305 — 8 oz.
GRAPEFRUIT — CEREAL
Packs 4 doz.—37#

G300 — 15 oz.
BOWL
Packs 4 doz.—43#

G297 — 6¾"
PIE OR SALAD PLATE
Packs 4 doz.—35#

G306 — 9"
DINNER PLATE
Packs 2 doz.—31#

IMPRESSIVE VARIETY BOOSTS SALES

"JANE-RAY"
(1945-1963)
G-3800

Production of this pattern began in 1945, and at that time it was the only heat-proof dinnerware made in an attractive jade color, (JADE-ITE or G3800 LINE as ANCHOR HOCKING referred to it). "Jane-Ray" has that beautiful shade of green which compliments that corner cabinet, or that old pie safe which belonged to Grandma. Even if it's not an honored family heirloom you have in your kitchen, this pattern, placed in any china cabinet, will certainly catch anyone's eye who enters the room.

This is an excellent pattern of "FIRE-KING" for the new collector to begin his or her collection. Most items are easy to find with the exception of a few. The sugar bowl with a good lid is one of the harder pieces to find, because the lid is often chipped or missing. Also, as with most of the patterns, bowls are more scarce, with the exception of the 5 7/8" cereal bowls. These were given away as premiums with the purchase of any size bag of "TOWN CRYER FLOUR". There is also a demi-tasse cup and saucer in the "Jane-Ray" design that is a jewel to add to anyone's collection. These pieces are difficult to find, but with hard work and a little bit of luck, they can be found.

"Jane-Ray" is very easy to recognize once you've been introduced. It has a noticeable ribbed design molded into the outer edge of the plate, bowl and saucer. The cup, sugar, and creamer however, will be ribbed on the outside from the top to the bottom. There are two shades of jade-ite in this pattern. One has a lighter color and a very deep ribbed design, the other is a darker color with a very shallow ribbed design.

Trademarks of this pattern, as with all "FIRE-KING" glassware, are located on the bottom of each item. The markings for this pattern are as follows: (OVEN Fire-King GLASS) the oldest, (OVEN Fire-King WARE), (OVEN Fire-King WARE MADE IN U.S.A.), bullseye design (with heavy ribbed design around the edge), and a plain bottom with no trademark.

Anchor Hocking made a jade-ite coffee mug and cereal bowl that were sold as a set. This 8 oz. mug and 5" cereal bowl goes great with the Jane-Ray pattern, so don't hesitate to add it to your set.

In our many trips to glass shows, flea markets, antique shops, and malls, thrift stores, junk shops and Grandma's kitchen cabinets, we have ran across a few unusual pieces. We found an ivory dinner plate in the "Jane-Ray" pattern at a Flea Market in Charlotte, North Carolina. The lady we bought it from said she had owned the whole set. There are several mixing bowls that were made with the deep ribbed pattern of "Jane-Ray", in jade-ite, ivory, forest green and clear.

PRICE GUIDE

DESCRIPTION		CURRENT PRICES
CUP	- 8 oz.	— $3.00
SAUCER	- 5 ¾"	— 1.00
PLATE, SALAD	- 7 ¾"	— 4.00
PLATE, DINNER	- 9 1/8"	— 6.00
PLATTER	- 9"x 12"	— 10.00
BOWL, DESSERT	- 4 7/8"	— 3.00
BOWL, CEREAL	- 5 7/8"	— 4.50
BOWL, SOUP	- 7 5/8"	— 6.50
BOWL, VEGETABLE	- 8 ¼"	— 10.00
SUGAR, W/LID*	-	— 7.00
CREAMER	-	— 5.00
CUP, DEMI.	- 3 ½ oz.	— 12.00
SAUCER, DEMI.	- 4 ½"	— 7.00
MUG, PLAIN	- 8 oz.	— 3.00
BOWL, CHILI	- 5"	— 3.00

*Sugar Without Lid Deduct $3.00

Jade-ite Fire-King Dinnerware

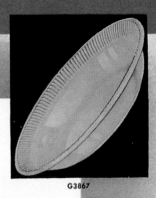

G3879 — G3829   G3874 — G3875   G3838 — G3841   G3867

PACKING

G3879—	Cup	6 doz. — 24 lbs.
G3829—	Saucer	6 doz. — 29 lbs.
G3874—4 ⅞″	Dessert	6 doz. — 25 lbs.
G3875—5 ⅞″	Cereal or Oatmeal	6 doz. — 36 lbs.
G3838—7 ¾″	Salad Plate	3 doz. — 26 lbs.
G3841—9 ⅛″	Dinner Plate	3 doz. — 39 lbs.
G3867—7 ⅝″	Soup Plate	3 doz. — 29 lbs.

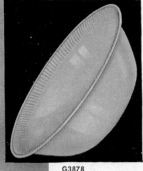

G3878   G3847   G3853 — G3854

G3878— 8 ¼″	Vegetable Bowl	1 doz. — 15 lbs.
G3847—12 x 9″	Platter	1 doz. — 21 lbs.
G3853—	Sugar & Cover	3 doz. — 22 lbs.
G3854—	Creamer	3 doz. — 16 lbs.

PREPACKED SET

G3800—12 Pce. Starter Set

Each Set in Gift Box, 6 Sets to Shipping Carton — 49 lbs.

COMPOSITION:
Four G3879 Cups
Four G3829 Saucers
Four G3841 Dinner Plates

See Page 18 for Jade-ite St. Denis Cup and Saucer.

G3800

HEAT-RESISTANT

JADE-ITE HEAT-PROOF DINNERWARE

20 PIECE DINNER SET — GIFT PACKED

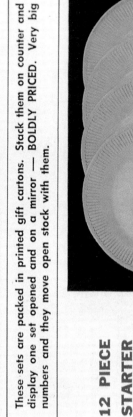

G3800/4 — 20 Pce.
DINNER SET
Each Set Pkd. in Gift Ctn.,
4 Sets to R/S Ctn.—48#

COMPOSITION:
Four Cups
Four Saucers
Four Desserts
Four Salad Plates
Four Dinner Plates

These sets are packed in printed gift cartons. Stack them on counter and display one set opened and on a mirror — BOLDLY PRICED. Very big numbers and they move open stock with them.

12 PIECE STARTER SET

G3800 — 12 Pce.
STARTER SET
Each Set Pkd. in Gift Ctn.,
6 Sets to R/S Ctn.—46#

COMPOSITION:
Four Cups
Four Saucers
Four Plates

Gift Packed

JADE-ITE HEAT-PROOF DINNERWARE

A FAST-MOVING LINE EVERYWHERE

G3838 — 7¾″ Salad Plate
Packs 3 doz.—25#

G3841 — 9⅛″ Dinner Plate
Packs 3 doz.—36#

G3878 — 8¼″ Vegetable Bowl
Packs 1 doz.—13#

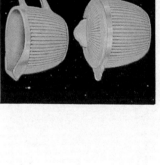

G3853 — Sugar and Cover
Packs 3 doz.—24#

G3854 — Creamer
Packs 3 doz.—16#

G3874 — 4⅞″ Dessert
Packs 6 doz.—22#

G3875—5⅝″ Cereal or Oatmeal
Packs 6 doz.—38#

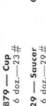

G3879 — Cup
Packs 6 doz.—23#

G3829 — Saucer
Packs 6 doz.—29#

G3867 — 7⅝″ Soup Plate
Packs 3 doz.—27#

G3847 — 12″x9″ Platter
Packs 1 doz.—19#

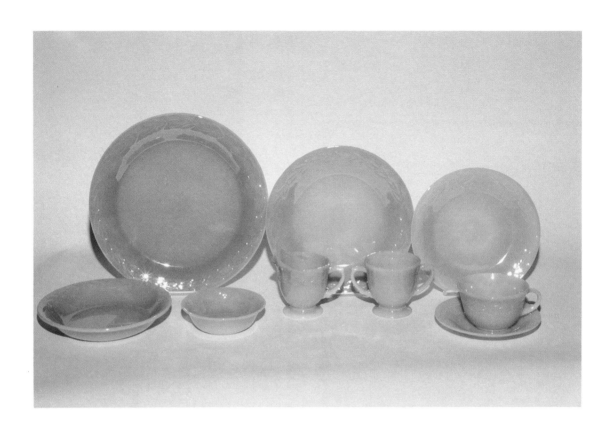

"GRAY LAUREL"
(1953-1954)
LINE #K4300

"Gray Laurel" is easily recognized by it's gray color, and the laurel leaf band around the perimeter of each piece. This is another pattern that is very hard to find in good condition, due to it's sensitivity to strong cleaners and abrasives. But when found in new condition it makes a beautiful table setting.

The hard to find pieces are, the bowls (with the desserts being the easiest to find) and the 11" serving plate.

The trademark found on this pattern is, (OVEN Fire-King WARE MADE IN U.S.A.).

PRICE GUIDE			
DESCRIPTION		CURRENT PRICES	
CUP	- 8 oz.	—	$3.00
SAUCER	- 5 7/8"	—	2.00
PLATE, SALAD	- 7 ¾"	—	4.00
PLATE, DINNER	- 9 1/8"	—	6.00
PLATE, SERVING	- 11"	—	8.00
BOWL, DESSERT	- 4 7/8"	—	3.50
BOWL, SOUP	- 7 5/8"	—	5.00
BOWL, VEGETABLE	- 8 ¼"	—	8.00
SUGAR, FOOTED	- (Open)	—	4.00
CREAMER, FOOTED	-	—	4.00

"IVORY LAUREL"
(1952-1953)
W4300

This pattern has been the most elusive color of the laurel series of tableware to locate. In five years of looking we have found only the sugar, creamer, and a few saucers. We have not found any catalog listings or magazine ads. But they've got to be out there somewhere. We're not about to give up!

The trademark found on this pattern is, (OVEN Fire-King WARE MADE IN U.S.A.).

PRICE GUIDE			
DESCRIPTION		CURRENT PRICES	
CUP	- 8 oz.	—	$3.00
SAUCER	- 5 7/8"	—	2.00
PLATE, SALAD	- 7 ¾"	—	4.00
PLATE, DINNER	- 9 1/8"	—	6.00
PLATE, SERVING	- 11"	—	8.00
BOWL, DESSERT	- 4 7/8"	—	3.50
BOWL, SOUP	- 7 5/8"	—	5.00
BOWL, VEGETABLE	- 8 ¼"	—	8.00
SUGAR, FOOTED	- (Open)	—	4.00
CREAMER, FOOTED	-	—	4.00

"PEACH LUSTRE"
(1951-1965)
L4300

The color used in this pattern is called "Lustre" by Anchor Hocking in every case with the exception of the ovenware, which they refer to as copper-tint. The "L" in the line number stands for lustre and the 4300 for the laurel design casting.

The lustre finish used on this pattern is very easily scratched, and faded by the use of strong cleaning materials. This fact makes "Peach Lustre" hard to find in good condition. With this pattern they changed the platter from an oval 9"x12" to an 11" serving plate.

The trademark found on this pattern is, (OVEN Fire-King WARE MADE IN U.S.A.).

We found two large sets of "Peach Lustre" with the labels still intact. The labels read, (Peach Lustre heat-proof Anchorglass Anchor Hocking Glass Corp. Lancaster Ohio U.S.A.), and are gold, red, and black in color. Also, some of the labeled pieces have a light foggy color around the laurel band.

There are quite a few accessory pieces in the Peach Lustre color. You will find them listed in the Novelties section.

PRICE GUIDE

DESCRIPTION		CURRENT PRICES
CUP	- 8 oz.	— $3.00
SAUCER	- 5 7/8"	— 2.00
PLATE, SALAD	- 7 ¾"	— 4.00
PLATE, DINNER	- 9 1/8"	— 6.00
PLATE, SERVING	- 11"	— 8.00
BOWL, DESSERT	- 4 7/8"	— 3.50
BOWL, SOUP	- 7 5/8"	— 5.00
BOWL, VEGETABLE	- 8 ¼"	— 8.00
SUGAR, FOOTED	- (Open)	— 4.00
CREAMER, FOOTED	-	— 4.00

"ROYAL LUSTRE"
(1976)
W3400   L3400

"Royal Lustre" has a ribbed pattern similar to "Jane-Ray" but with a scalloped edge and a peach lustre color. The cups look more like a mug than a cup. The sugar looks like a cup without a handle and has a flat topped knob lid. The creamer is a cup with a spout. There is also a demi-cup and saucer.

The hard to find items are the bowls, platter, and the sugar with a lid. There are very few pieces of this set marked "FIRE-KING".

The trademarks found on this set are, (ANCHOR HOCKING [anchor over H symbol] Fire-King OVEN-PROOF, mold #, MADE IN U.S.A.), and (ANCHOR HOCKING [anchor over H symbol] Suburbia OVEN-PROOF, mold #, MADE IN U.S.A.).

PRICE GUIDE

DESCRIPTION		CURRENT PRICES
CUP	- 8 oz.	— $2.00
SAUCER	- 5 ¾"	— 1.00
PLATE, SALAD	- 3 ¼"	— 3.00
PLATE, DINNER	- 10"	— 5.00
PLATTER, OVAL	- 9 ½"x 13"	— 6.00
BOWL, DESSERT	- 4 ¾"	— 3.00
BOWL, SOUP	- 6 3/8"	— 5.00
BOWL, VEGETABLE	- 8 ½"	— 6.00
SUGAR, LID*	-	— 4.00
CREAMER	-	— 4.00
CUP, DEMITASSE	- 3 ¼ oz.	— 3.00
SAUCER, DEMITASSE	- 4 ¾"	— 1.00

*Sugar without lid deduct $1.00.

PEACH LUSTRE DINNERWARE

PREPACKED SET

L4300/33—18 Pce. Luncheon Set

Each Set in Gift Carton, 4 Sets to Shipping Carton — 41 lbs.

COMPOSITION:

Four L4379 Cups	Four L4341 Dinner Plates
Four L4329 Saucers	One L4353 Sugar
Four L4374 Desserts	One L4354 Creamer

A Popular Coffee Mug and Cereal Bowl in Peach Lustre are shown on Page 9. See the French Casserole and Cover on Page 47.

OPEN STOCK

L4379 — L4329

L4374

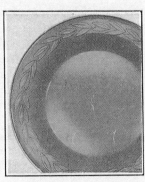

L4338 — L4341 — L4346

PACKING

L4379—	8 oz.	Cup	6 doz. — 25 lbs.
L4329—	5¾″	Saucer	6 doz. — 28 lbs.
L4374—	4⅞″	Dessert	6 doz. — 23 lbs.
L4338—	7¾″	Salad Plate	3 doz. — 28 lbs.
L4341—	9⅛″	Dinner Plate	3 doz. — 37 lbs.
L4346—	11″	Serving Plate	1 doz. — 20 lbs.

L4367

L4378

L4353 — L4354

L4367—	7⅝″	Soup Plate	3 doz. — 29 lbs.
L4378—	8¼″	Vegetable Bowl	1 doz. — 14 lbs.
L4353—		Sugar	2 doz. — 11 lbs.
L4354—		Creamer	2 doz. — 10 lbs.

HEAT-PROOF

HEAT-PROOF

7.

ROYAL LUSTRE

FP

1975 Anchor Hocking Catalog

125

"MEADOW GREEN"
(1968-1976)
W4600/75

"Meadow Green" is without a doubt the most popular pattern in the 4600 line of dinnerware. It has a circular floral design in the center of the plates using three shades of green that matched the avocado fad so popular at the time of it's issue. This is one of the few patterns that has a matching set of ovenware along with several open stock items.

Like the other patterns of the 4600 line there isn't a lot of "Meadow Green" showing up at the present. But given a little more time there should be a wealth of it on the market.

The trademarks found on this pattern are, (ANCHOR HOCKING [anchor over H symbol] Fire-King WARE, mold #, MADE IN U.S.A.), and (ANCHOR HOCKING [anchor H symbol] Fire-King DINNERWARE, mold #, MADE IN U.S.A.).

PRICE GUIDE

DESCRIPTION		CURRENT PRICES
CUP, STACKING	- 7½ oz.	— $2.00
SAUCER	- 5 ¾"	— 1.00
PLATE, SALAD	- 7 3/8"	— 3.00
PLATE, DINNER	- 10"	— 4.00
PLATTER, OVAL	- 9"x 12"	— 5.00
BOWL, DESSERT	- 4 5/8"	— 3.00
BOWL, SOUP	- 6 5/8"	— 5.00
BOWL, VEGETABLE	- 8 ¼"	— 6.00
SUGAR, LID	-	— 4.00
CREAMER	-	— 4.00

Sugar Without Lid Deduct $1.00.

OVENWARE

PRICE GUIDE

DESCRIPTION		CURRENT PRICES
CASSEROLE, White Knob Lid	- 1 qt.	— $4.00
CASSEROLE, White Knob Lid	- 1½ qt.	— 5.00
CASSEROLE, White Knob Lid	- 1½ qt. (Oval)	— 6.00
CASSEROLE, White Knob Lid	- 2 qt.	— 6.00
CASSEROLE, White Knob Lid	- 3 qt.	— 7.00
DISH, UTILITY BAKING	- 1½ qt.	— 5.00
DISH, UTILITY BAKING	- 2 qt.	— 6.00
CAKE DISH, Round	- 8"	— 5.00
CAKE DISH, Square	- 8"	— 5.00
DISH, DEEP LOAF	- 5"x9"	— 5.00
INDIVIDUAL CASSEROLE (W/Handle)	- 12 oz.	— 3.00
CUSTARD	- 6 oz.	— 1.00
BOWL, SOUP/CEREAL	- 8 oz.	— 3.00
MUG	- 8 oz.	— 3.00

MEADOW GREEN DINNERWARE

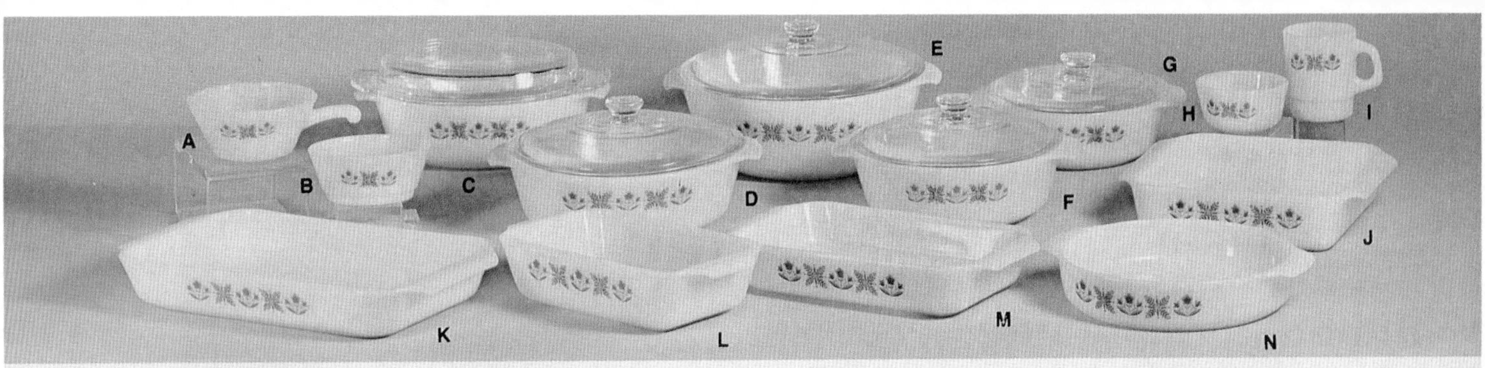

MEADOW GREEN OVENWARE

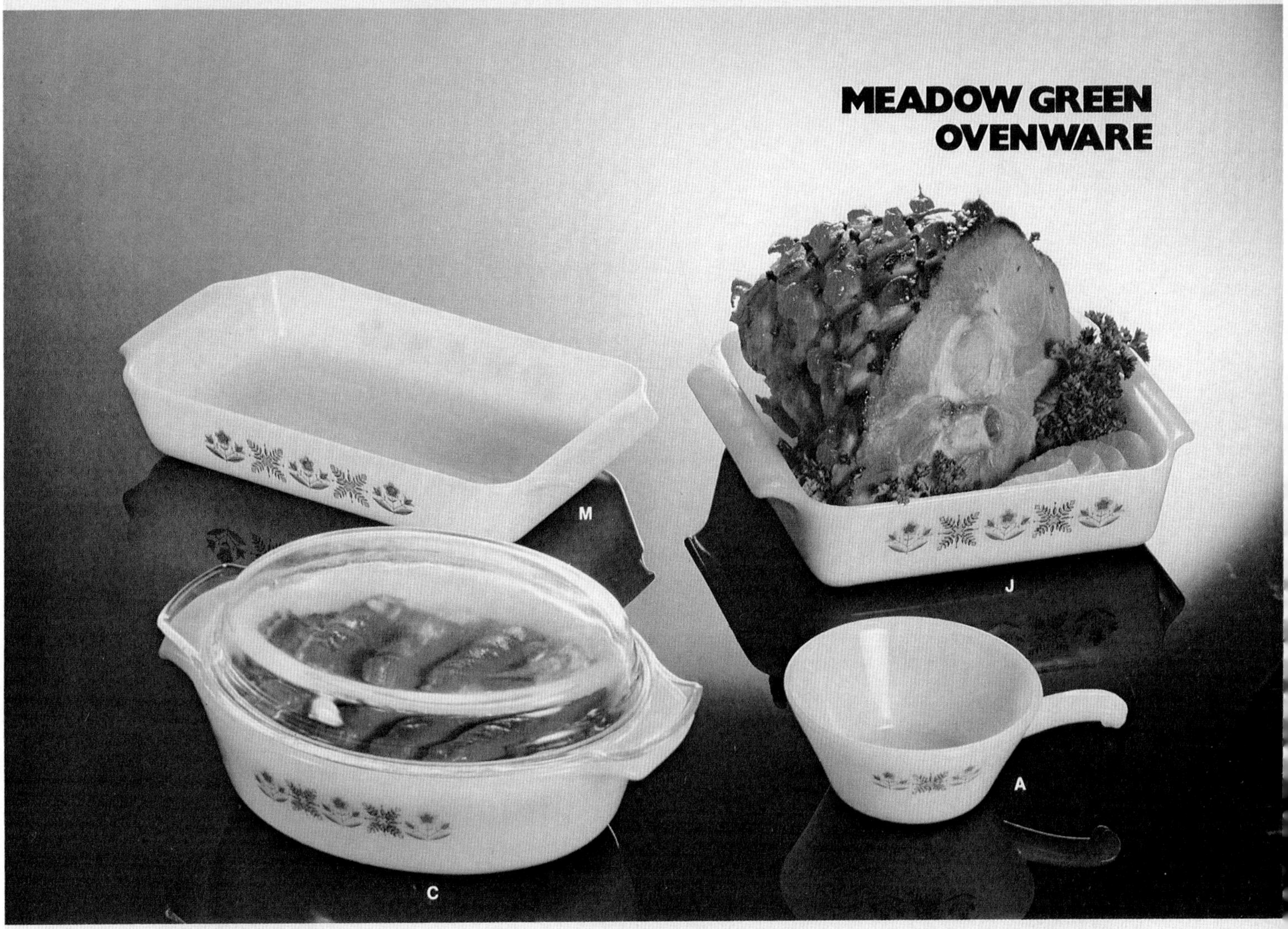

BULK PACKED (BY DOZEN)

photo ref.	description	item order no.	shipper doz.	shipper lbs.	price doz.
A	12 oz. individual casserole	W240E/75	2	17	
B	5" soup/cereal	W310/75	2	13	
C	1½ qt. oval casserole/au gratin cover	WH433/75	½	22	
D	2 qt. casserole/cover	WH438/75	½	25	
E	3 qt. casserole/cover	WH439/75	½	33	
F	1½ qt. casserole/cover	WH437/75	½	21	
G	1 qt. casserole/cover	WH436/75	½	17	
H	6 oz. custard	W434/75	4	19	
I	9 oz. mug	W312/75	2	15	
J	8" square cake dish	W435/75	½	18	
K	2 qt. utility baking dish	W431/75	½	22	
L	5 x 9" deep loaf pan	W441/75	½	12	
M	1½ qt. utility baking dish	W432/75	½	15	
N	9" round cake dish	W429/75	½	14	

NOTE: See index for additional listings of Meadow Green bulk and gift items.

"MILK WHITE"
(1950's)
W1700

One of the first pieces of "FIRE-KING" we bought was a "Milk White" saucer. We gave ten cents for it at an old country flea market. At that time, we didn't know anyone who collected "FIRE-KING" and most collectors considered it junk dishes. But we liked it because it was inexpensive, and we felt it would become collectible in time. We also liked the ease with which it could be identified, just turn over the piece and there you would find the words "FIRE-KING".

The hard to locate pieces are the bowls, sugar and creamer, and the dinner plates. In five years of looking, we have just lately found four good plates. The reason for this, we do not know. Maybe we just didn't look in the right places.

The trademark you will find most often will be, (OVEN Fire-king WARE MADE IN U.S.A.) with some of the newer pieces having Anchor Hocking over the trademarks.

There are quite a few accessory items found in "Milk White" that you will not find in any other color. The gravy boat being one of them. There is also a very large footed platter with a well & tree design. This makes a very good turkey platter.

PRICE GUIDE

DESCRIPTION		CURRENT PRICES
CUP	- 8 oz.	— $2.00
SAUCER	- 5 ¾"	— 1.00
PLATE, SALAD	- 7 ¾"	— 2.00
PLATE, DINNER	- 9 1/8"	— 4.00
PLATTER, OVAL	- 9"x 12"	— 5.00
BOWL, DESSERT	- 4 ¼"	— 2.00
BOWL, CEREAL	- 5 7/8"	— 3.00
BOWL, SOUP	- 7 ½"	— 4.00
BOWL, VEGETABLE	-	— 5.00
SUGAR, OPEN	-	— 3.00
CREAMER	-	— 3.00
MUG	- 8 oz.	— 2.50
BOWL, CHILI	- 5"	— 3.00
GRAVY BOAT	-	— 10.00
PLATTER, WELL & TREE	- 14¾"x10 7/8"	— 15.00

"MILKWHITE" TABLEWARE
(1956-1957)
W4000

This is another of the lost tableware sets. Anchor Hocking made a wealth of special order glass that was used for premiums or given away with the purchase of everything from gas to groceries and soap to oatmeal. Unfortunately a lot of this glass was never listed in Anchor Hocking's sales catalogs. The records of those who ordered this glass and what it was used for is buried in old files that have been either stored or discarded many years ago.

The production date of this glass was most likely in the mid to late 50's, due to the use of 4000 series molds and by the trademarks found on this set. As always, please feel free to drop a line or give us a call if you should have any information you would like to share on this pattern or any other pattern of "FIRE-KING" glassware.

The trademark found on this pattern is, (OVEN Fire-King WARE MADE IN U.S.A.).

As for the hard to find pieces, the bowls will be the hardest to locate.

PRICE GUIDE

DESCRIPTION		CURRENT PRICES
CUP	- 8 oz.	— $3.00
SAUCER	- 5 ¾"	— 1.50
PLATE, BREAD & BUTTER	- 6 ¼"	— 3.00
PLATE, SALAD	- 7 ¼"	— 4.00
PLATE, DINNER	- 9"	— 6.00
PLATE, SERVING	- 10"	— 8.00
BOWL, DESSERT	- 4 5/8"	— 3.00
BOWL, SOUP	- 6 5/8"	— 6.00
BOWL, VEGETABLE	- 8 ¼"	— 10.00
SUGAR, Open	-	— 4.00
CREAMER	-	— 4.00

"PRIMROSE"
(1960-1962)
W4600

"Primrose" is one of the attractive floral designs Anchor Hocking introduced in the late 50's. Not only did this pattern of tableware have a snack set, but it also had a candlewarmer, set of casseroles and an 11 piece set of ovenware.

"Primrose" can be identified by the large cluster of red and pink flowers with gray leaves and black stems on milk white "FIRE-KING" glassware. The floral design was applied to the center of the plates and bowls, to the side of the cups, sugar and creamer, and the inner rim of the saucer. The ovenware has the design on two sides of each piece.

The trademark found on this pattern is (OVEN Fire-King WARE MADE IN U.S.A.), with a mold number between the WARE and MADE IN U.S.A.

The difficult to find pieces of "Primrose" are the bread and butter plate, soup bowl, vegetable bowl in the tableware, the 1 pt. casserole, the 2 qt. casserole, and the 5" x 9" deep loaf with lid in the ovenware. As with all the floral patterns a lot of the heavily used pieces will be faded. We have been able to find a lot of mint condition pieces, and there are still some boxed sets out there.

PRICE GUIDE

DESCRIPTION		CURRENT PRICES
CUP	- 8 oz.	— $3.00
SAUCER	- 5 ¾"	— 1.00
PLATE, BREAD & BUTTER	- 6 ¼"	— 2.00
PLATE, SALAD	- 7 3/8"	— 3.00
PLATE, DINNER	- 9 1/8"	— 5.00
PLATTER, OVAL	- 9" x 12"	— 6.00
BOWL, DESSERT	- 4 5/8"	— 3.00
BOWL, SOUP	- 6 5/8"	— 6.00
BOWL, VEGETABLE	- 8 ¼"	— 6.00
SUGAR & LID*	-	— 4.00
CREAMER	-	— 3.00
PLATE, SNACK SET	- 6"x11"	— 3.00
CUP, SNACK SET	- 5 oz.	— 1.50

*Sugar without lid deduct $1.00.

"PRIMROSE" OVENWARE

PRICE GUIDE

DESCRIPTION		CURRENT PRICES
DESSERT	- 6 oz.	— $3.00
CASSEROLE & LID	- 1 pt.	— 4.00
CASSEROLE & LID	- 1 qt.	— 5.00
CASSEROLE & LID	- 1 ½ qt.	— 5.00
CASSEROLE & LID, OVAL	- 1 ½ qt.	— 5.00
CASSEROLE & LID	- 2 qt.	— 6.00
CAKE PAN, ROUND	- 8"	— 5.00
CAKE PAN, SQUARE	- 8"	— 5.00
PAN, DEEP LOAF & LID	- 5" x 9"	— 6.00
PAN, UTILITY BAKING	- 6½" x 10½"	— 5.00
PAN, UTILITY BAKING	- 8" x 12½"	— 6.00

PRIMROSE ANCHORWHITE DINNERWARE

W4679/62 — W4629/62

W4674/62

W4638/62 — W4641/62

PACKING

W4679/62—8 oz. Cup	6 doz.	27 lbs.
W4629/62—5¾" Saucer	6 doz.	27 lbs.
W4674/62—4⅝" Dessert	6 doz.	21 lbs.
W4638/62—7⅜" Salad Plate	3 doz.	23 lbs.
W4641/62—9⅛" Dinner Plate	3 doz.	36 lbs.

W4667/62

W4678/62

W4647/62

W4667/62— 6⅝" Soup Plate	3 doz.	26 lbs.
W4678/62— 8¼" Vegetable Bowl	1 doz.	14 lbs.
W4647/62—12 x 9" Platter	1 doz.	20 lbs.

W4653/62 — W4654/62

W183/62 — W181/62

W4653/62— Sugar & Cover	2 doz.	16 lbs.
W4654/62— Creamer	2 doz.	12 lbs.
W183/62— 5 oz. Fruit Juice	3 doz.	12 lbs.
W181/62—11 oz. Tumbler	3 doz.	20 lbs.

HEAT-PROOF   HEAT-PROOF

34.

"PRIMROSE" ANCHORWHITE OVENWARE

W424/62

W405/62 — W406/62

W407/62 — W408/62

PACKING

W424/62—6	oz.	Dessert or Low Custard	4 doz. — 14 lbs.
W405/62—1	Pt.	Casserole—Knob Cover	1 doz. — 17 lbs.
W406/62—1	Qt.	Casserole—Knob Cover	½ doz. — 14 lbs.
W407/62—1 ½	Qt.	Casserole—Knob Cover	½ doz. — 19 lbs.
W408/62—2	Qt.	Casserole—Knob Cover	½ doz. — 22 lbs.

All Covers are Clear Crystal Fire-King.

W467/62

W450/62

W452/62

W467/62—1 ½	Qt.	Oval Casserole—Au Gratin Cover	½ doz. — 19 lbs.
W450/62—8"		Round Cake Pan	½ doz. — 12 lbs.
W452/62—8"		Square Cake Pan	½ doz. — 17 lbs.

See Pages 48 and 49 for "Primrose" Dinnerware.

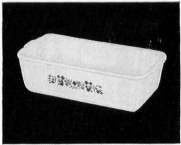

W409/62

W410/62 — W411/62

W409/62—5x9"	Deep Loaf Pan	½ doz. — 12 lbs.
W410/62—6 ½ x10 ½"	Utility Baking Pan	½ doz. — 15 lbs.
W411/62—8x12 ½"	Utility Baking Pan	½ doz. — 22 lbs.

"Fire-King" — The World's Finest Baking Ware. Also available in Crystal, Anchorwhite and Copper-Tint.

GUARANTEED 2 YEARS AGAINST OVEN BREAKAGE. To be replaced Free by dealer in exchange for broken pieces.

See Prepacked Sets on Page 65.

64.

"ROYAL RUBY"
(1956-1957)
R4000

This is one of the lost tableware sets made by Anchor Hocking. That is to say it is not listed in any catalog, which means it was a special order set and never offered as open stock. It was made using the same molds as the "Turquoise Blue" dinnerware or 4000 series line. This would place it's time of production in the late 50's.

This set did not have trademarks embossed on it and we have not found any labeled pieces. Nor have we been able to find any catalog listings or sales ads. However, it is assumed that if found with labels they would be the standard "Royal Ruby" labels.

As for the hard to find pieces, the mid size bowls seem to be the most scarce. Listed below are the pieces we have been able to locate.

PRICE GUIDE

DESCRIPTION		CURRENT PRICES
CUP	- 8 oz.	— $4.00
SAUCER	- 5¾"	— 3.00
PLATE, SALAD	- 7¼"	— 5.00
PLATE, DINNER	- 9"	— 10.00
BOWL, DESSERT	- 4 5/8"	— 4.50
BOWL, CHILI	- 5"	— 6.00
BOWL, CEREAL	- 6 5/8"	— 8.00
BOWL, VEGETABLE	- 8 ¼"	— 12.00
SUGAR, (Open)	-	— 6.00
CREAMER	-	— 6.00

✭✭✭

"ROYAL RUBY"
(1940's)
R1700

The 1700 line of "Royal Ruby" glassware is one of the first tableware sets to use the famous "FIRE-KING" formula of glass. Although it did not have the "FIRE-KING" trademark embossed on the bottom, it had the same versatile strength and beauty as the "Sapphire Blue Ovenware". It's distinctive dark red color has made it one of the most sought after colors of glassware on the market today.

As for trademarks, "Royal Ruby" is not marked. But if found with the original labels, they read (ROYAL RUBY/ANCHORGLASS Anchor Hocking Glass Corp. Lancaster Ohio U.S.A.).

Most of this pattern can be found quite easily. Almost every antique shop or mall will have plenty of "Royal Ruby" on hand. But you will have to get off of your billfold just a little to complete your set. Popularity of any pattern will tend to increase it's asking price.

PRICE GUIDE

DESCRIPTION		CURRENT PRICES
CUP	- 8 oz.	— $4.00
SAUCER	- 5¾ oz.	— 2.00
PLATE, SALAD	- 7¾"	— 4.00
PLATE, DINNER	- 9 1/8"	— 10.00
BOWL, FRUIT	- 4¼"	— 4.50
BOWL, SOUP	- 7½"	— 10.00
BOWL, VEGETABLE	- 8½"	— 20.00
SUGAR, FOOTED & LID*		— 6.00
CREAMER, FOOTED		— 6.00

*Sugar without lid deduct $3.00.

"SHEATH OF WHEAT"
(1957-1959)
G4700

"Sheath of Wheat" appears to be a collectors nickname. As with most of the glassware Anchor Hocking made for sales premiums, it was listed by it's line number only. The G4700 line was a special order for the National Oat Co.

This pattern was made in jade-ite and clear, with the exception of the tumblers which were made in clear only. The sheaths of wheat embossing encircles each piece. The plate and saucer has small notches spaced along the outer edges similar to those found on the "Alice" pattern.

As for hard to find pieces, anything in jade-ite is going to be hard to locate. The jade-ite snack tray and bowl, or nappie if you prefer, are the rarest pieces of this pattern. The clear pieces are the most common, thus the easiest set to complete, with possibly the 9" plate being the one exception.

As with most patterns sold for use as a premium, there is no trademark found on this pattern.

PRICE GUIDE

DESCRIPTION		CURRENT PRICES		
		CLEAR/JADE-ITE		
CUP	- 6½ oz.	— $3.00	—	$5.00
SAUCER	- 6"	— 1.50	—	3.00
PLATE	- 9"	— 5.00	—	7.00
BOWL, NAPPIE	- 4½"	— 3.00	—	6.00
TRAY, SNACK	- 7" x 10"	— 5.00	—	10.00
TUMBLER, JUICE, Clear	- 6 oz.	— 3.00		
TUMBLER, WATER, Clear	- 9 oz.	— 5.00		

∿∿

"SUNRISE"
(1951-1953)
W4100

Anchor Hocking made this pattern with a swirl design molded into the glass, reaching from the outer rim to just off center in each item. Then a bright red color, about the color of an early morning sunrise, was added to the outer rim of each piece. Also embossed on the bottom of each piece is the trademark; ("OVEN Fire-King WARE MADE IN U.S.A.").

Originally this pattern, like many others, could be purchased many different ways. If you had the money, you could buy whole place settings of "Sunrise" at your favorite five-and-dime store, or some other department store. Chances are you grew up through hard times, just as we did, and you purchased only things necessary to get you by. Sometimes when you went to that old country grocery store, you might notice a new brand of flour, oats, washing powders, etc. with premiums or coupons inside to order items needed for the house. "Sunrise" tableware, for example, was also purchased with coupons that were placed in packages of "Nun-Better" flour. Since "Nun-Better" flour was sold mostly in the northern states, it stands to reason that more items of "Sunrise" will be found in the north.

Like most tableware sets, the bowls are the hardest to come by. If you look closely at the red border of the oval platter you will notice that it look's like it was painted by a different method than than the rest of the tableware. The first time we saw it, we thought it was an "Ivory Swirl" platter that someone had painted by hand to fake a "Sunrise" platter.

The Anchor Hocking Ivory color used for this set, with it's red border makes a very attractive table setting for that old country look. So get out there and dig through those dust covered back shelves, and just maybe everyone else has over looked that boxed set of "Sunrise" Tableware. By the way, watch out for those crazy folks crawling around on the floor, looking under the bottom shelves, that's probably us.

PRICE GUIDE

DESCRIPTION		CURRENT PRICES	DESCRIPTION		CURRENT PRICES
CUP	- 8 oz.	— $3.00	BOWL, DESSERT	- 4 7/8"	— $3.50
SAUCER	- 5 ¾"	— 2.00	BOWL, CEREAL	- 5 7/8"	— 4.00
PLATE, SALAD	- 7 ¾"	— 4.00	BOWL, SOUP	- 7 5/8"	— 6.00
PLATE, DINNER	- 9 1/8"	— 6.00	BOWL, VEGETABLE	- 8 ¼"	— 10.00
PLATTER, OVAL	- 9"x 12"	— 10.00	SUGAR & LID*	-	— 6.00
*Sugar Without Lid Deduct $2.00			CREAMER	-	— 5.00

"GOLDEN SHELL"
(1963-1976)
W2300

The W2300 line can be easily identified by it's milk white color in a swirl design and 22k gold scalloped edge. This pattern is often confused with the older 22k "Gold" (W4100) pattern tableware. The main difference being, the scalloped edge on the W2300 pattern tableware, and the measurements are different for each piece.

The hard to find pieces are the bowls, with the vegetable and the soup harder to locate. Also it is a bit of a challenge to find all the pieces marked "FIRE-KING", again because Anchor Hocking dropped the "FIRE-KING" trademark sometime in the late 60's.

The trademarks found on this pattern are, (ANCHOR HOCKING [anchor over H symbol] Fire-King WARE MADE IN U.S.A.), (ANCHOR HOCKING [anchor over H symbol] Fire-King dinnerware, mold #, MADE IN U.S.A.), (ANCHOR HOCKING [anchor over H symbol] Fire-King OVEN-PROOF, mold #, MADE IN U.S.A.), and (ANCHOR HOCKING [anchor over H symbol] Suburbia OVEN-PROOF, mold #, MADE IN U.S.A.).

PRICE GUIDE

DESCRIPTION		CURRENT PRICES	
CUP	- 8 oz.	—	$3.00
SAUCER	- 5 ¾"	—	1.50
PLATE, SALAD	- 7 ¼"	—	3.00
PLATE, DINNER	- 10"	—	5.00
PLATTER, OVAL	- 9 ½"x 12"	—	6.00
BOWL, DESSERT	- 4 ¾"	—	3.00
BOWL, SOUP	- 6 3/8"	—	5.00
BOWL, VEGETABLE	- 8 ½"	—	7.00
SUGAR, LID*	-	—	4.00
CREAMER	-	—	4.00
CUP, DEMI.	- 3 ½ oz.	—	3.00
SAUCER, DEMI.	- 4 ¾"	—	1.50
SNACK PLATE	- 10"	—	4.50
SNACK CUP	- 8 oz.	—	3.00

*Sugar without lid deduct $1.00.

"JADE-ITE SHELL"
(1963-1967)
G2300

"Jade-ite Shell" is identified by it's jade-ite color in a swirl design with a scalloped edge. The cups have a sharply tapered design, almost funnel shape, with a small raised notch near the top and bottom of the handles. The sugar and creamer are footed with the same raised notches on the handles. Remember the scalloped edge, the footed sugar and creamer, and the tapered cup design are the main differences in the G2300 line from the older G4100 line.

The hard to find pieces are the bowls, platter, and the sugar with a lid. As with the other shell patterns, finding the pieces marked "FIRE-KING" is a little tough. This is due to the fact that Anchor Hocking stopped using the "FIRE-KING" trademark on most of its glassware sometime in the late 60's.

The trademarks found on this pattern are, (ANCHOR HOCKING [anchor over H symbol] Fire-King WARE MADE IN U.S.A.), (ANCHOR HOCKING [anchor over H symbol] Fire-King dinnerware, mold #, MADE IN U.S.A.), (ANCHOR HOCKING [anchor over H symbol] Fire-King OVEN-PROOF, mold #, MADE IN U.S.A.) and (ANCHOR HOCKING [anchor over H symbol] Suburbia OVEN-PROOF, mold # MADE IN U.S.A.).

PRICE GUIDE

DESCRIPTION		CURRENT PRICES	
CUP	- 8 oz.	—	$3.00
SAUCER	- 5 ¾"	—	1.50
PLATE, SALAD	- 7 ¼"	—	3.00
PLATE, DINNER	- 10"	—	5.00
PLATTER, OVAL	- 9½"x 13"	—	6.00
BOWL, DESSERT	- 4 ¾"	—	3.00
BOWL, SOUP	- 6 3/8"	—	5.00
BOWL, VEGETABLE	- 8 ½"	—	7.00
SUGAR, LID*	-	—	4.00
CREAMER	-	—	4.00
CUP, DEMI.	- 3½ oz.	—	3.00
SAUCER, DEMI.	- 4 ¾"	—	1.50

*Sugar without lid deduct $1.00.

Golden Shell Ovenproof Dinnerware

photo ref.	description	item order no.	shipper doz.	shipper lbs.	price doz.
			BULK PACKED (BY DOZEN)		
A	9½" x 13" platter	W2347/31	1	25	
B	10" dinner plate	W2346/31	3	47	
C	7¼" salad plate	W2338/31	3	26	
D	7⅝" soup bowl	W2368/31	3	29	
E	4¾" dessert	W2374/31	3	13	
F	8 oz. cup	W2379/31	3	15	
G	5¾" saucer	W2329/31	3	17	
H	6⅜" cereal	W2367/31	3	22	
I	Sugar/cover	W2353/31	1	10	
J	Creamer	W2354/31	1	7	
K	9" rim soup	W2366/31	3	34	
L	8½" vegetable bowl	W2378/31	1	14	

NOTE: *Blue item number indicates new product and/or packaging.*
See index for additional listings of Golden Shell gift items.

Tableware Bulk

T

jade-ite dinnerware

Heat-resistant; a soft jade-like lustre in English Regency styling. Great everyday ware, volume-priced. Open stock.

			Doz. Ctn.	Lbs. Ctn.
G2379		cup	3	14
G2329	5¾"	saucer	3	14
G2374	4¾"	dessert	3	13
G2367	6⅜"	cereal	3	22
G2338	7¼"	salad plate	3	23
G2368	7⅝"	soup plate	3	30
G2346	10"	dinner plate	3	43
G2378	8½"	vegetable bowl	1	14
G2347	13 x 9½"	platter	1	22
G2353		sugar/cover	1	9
G2354		creamer	1	6

Packed Sets

		Sets Ctn.	Lbs. Ctn.
G2300/5	12 pc starter set, printed parchment carton, 4 cups, 4 saucers, 4 din. plates	6	49

(See page 59 for Jade-ite St. Denis cups, mugs and bowls)

G2379   G2329

G2367   G2374   G2378

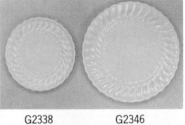

G2338   G2346

G2368

G2347

G2353   G2354

34

"LUSTRE SHELL"
(1965-1976)
L2300

"Lustre Shell" is identified by it's peach lustre or copper-tint color, whichever you prefer, on a swirl design and scalloped edge.

The hard to find items are the larger bowls, this could be because they didn't come with the smaller sets of tableware. As with all the shell (2300 line) glassware, finding all the pieces marked "FIRE-KING" is not easy. Due to Anchor Hocking's decision to drop the "FIRE-KING" trademark from most of it's glassware in the late 60's.

The trademarks found on this pattern are, (ANCHOR HOCKING [anchor over H symbol] Fire-King WARE MADE IN U.S.A.), (ANCHOR HOCKING [anchor over H symbol] Fire-King dinnerware, mold #, MADE IN U.S.A.), (ANCHOR HOCKING [anchor over H symbol] Fire-King OVEN-PROOF, mold #, MADE IN U.S.A.) and (ANCHOR HOCKING [anchor over H symbol] Suburbia OVEN-PROOF, mold #, MADE IN U.S.A.).

PRICE GUIDE

DESCRIPTION		CURRENT PRICES
CUP	- 8 oz.	— $3.00
SAUCER	- 8 ¾"	— 1.50
PLATE, SALAD	- 7 ¼"	— 3.00
PLATE, DINNER	- 10"	— 5.00
PLATTER, OVAL	- 9 ½"x13"	— 6.00
BOWL, DESSERT	- 4 ¾"	— 3.00
BOWL, SOUP	- 6 3/8"	— 5.00
BOWL, VEGETABLE	- 8 1/2"	— 7.00
SUGAR, LID*	-	— 4.00
CREAMER		— 4.00
CUP, DEMI.	- 3 ½ oz.	— 3.00
SAUCER, DEMI.	- 4 ¾"	— 1.50

*Sugar without lid deduct $1.00.

LUSTRE SHELL DINNERWARE

photo ref.	description	item order no.	shipper doz.	shipper lbs.	price doz.
	LUSTRE SHELL				
A	9½" x 13" platter	L2347	1	25	
B	10" dinner plate	L2346	3	50	
C	7¼" salad plate	L2338	3	25	
D	6⅜" cereal	L2367	3	27	
E	3¼ oz. demitasse cup	L2369	6	20	
F	4¾" demitasse saucer	L2339	6	19	
G	8 oz. cup	L2379	3	13	
H	5¾" saucer	L2329	3	18	
I	8½" vegetable bowl	L2378	1	15	
J	4¾" dessert	L2374	3	14	
K	7⅝" soup bowl	L2368	3	34	
L	9" rim soup	L2366	3	42	
M	Sugar/cover	L2353	1	10	
N	Creamer	L2354	1	7	
	PEACH LUSTRE				
O	9¾" divided dish	L898	1	23	
	In individual Gift Carton (not illustrated)	L898H	1	25	
P	5" soup/cereal bowl	L320	1	8	
Q	9 oz. mug	L319	2	15	
R	5" soup/cereal bowl	L291	2	15	
S	8 oz. mug	L1212	2	14	
T	8" bowl	L1678	1	17	
U	4½" bowl	L1664	3	15	

NOTE: See index for additional listings of Peach and Lustre bulk and gift items.

TABLEWARE BULK

98

"AZUR-ITE" (BLUE SWIRL)
(1949-1951)
A4100

"Azur-ite" or "Blue Swirl", as it's known by most collectors, is the first of the popular 4100 series pattern tableware to be made by Anchor Hocking. It is easily recognized by the distinctive 1" to 2" swirl pattern molded into the outer edge of the plates and bowls. The cup, sugar, and creamers have the swirl design from just below the rim to the bottom of each piece. As for trademarks there are only two, (OVEN Fire-King GLASS) and (OVEN Fire-King WARE). These markings are located on the bottom of each item.

"Azur-ite" is most often found one or two pieces at a time, but this is not to say complete sets cannot be found. Once we were traveling out of state looking for "FIRE-KING", when we came upon an old junk store that looked very promising. After entering the store we found it to be literally full of glassware. But, there was one problem, it was getting dark, and the store had no lights. Just as we were about to give up we noticed a very large stack of blue dishes sitting on a dust covered shelf. Further study of the pattern revealed it to be "Azur-ite" in an eight place setting, which included a very rare 9" flat flanged rim bowl. On a trip to Anchor Hocking, we were told that these 9" bowls were not a part of the original sets of dishes but, were sold as premiums with the purchase of flour, gasoline, etc. Whatever the case may be, one thing is for certain, to have found the 9" flanged bowl is a treasure in itself.

There are a few other items made in the azur-ite color, but were not swirl. There's a 5" cereal bowl that can be found quite easily. However, there should also be an 8 oz. mug that came with the bowl, as they were sold as sets. There is also a small leaf design bowl with a flared scalloped edge. We found one of these with the original label, that read (DOUBLE KAY NUT BOWL). We wonder if this bowl came with a plate as did other colors, (jade-ite, lustre).

PRICE GUIDE

DESCRIPTION		CURRENT PRICES		DESCRIPTION		CURRENT PRICES
CUP	- 8 oz.	— $4.00		BOWL, VEGETABLE	- 8 ¼"	— $12.00
SAUCER	- 5 ¾"	— 2.00		BOWL, FLANGED	- 9"	— 25.00
PLATE, SALAD	- 7 ¾"	— 4.00		BOWL, NUT		— 6.00
PLATE, DINNER	- 9 1/8"	— 6.00		BOWL, CHILI (NOT SWIRL)	- 5"	— 5.00
PLATTER, OVAL	- 9"x 12"	— 12.00		SUGAR, LID*	-	— 7.00
BOWL, DESSERT	- 4 7/8"	— 4.00		CREAMER	-	— 6.00
BOWL, CEREAL	- 5 7/8"	— 5.00				
BOWL, SOUP	- 7 5/8"	— 6.00				

*Sugar Without Lid Deduct $2.00

"IVORY SWIRL"
(1950-1958)
W4100

The "Ivory" tableware set was the second issue in the 4100 line, or "Swirl" pattern. The "W" in the line code stands for White or Ivory. In this case it stands for Ivory.

The trademarks found on this pattern are, (OVEN Fire-King GLASS) (OVEN Fire-King WARE), and (OVEN Fire-King WARE MADE IN U.S.A.).

The hard to find items are, the bowls, with the 5 7/8" cereal, and the 8 1/4" vegetable being the most elusive. Also, the sugar and creamer are not showing up very often.

We did have a minor problem finding the lid for the sugar. But about the time we had almost given up finding it without having to buy a complete set, we found one in a small antique shop not far from home. Only one thing was wrong. It was setting on the wrong sugar, an open sugar at that. We tried as hard as we could, and we could not convince the nice lady it did not go on that sugar. She just kept saying, "It fits it very nicely, thank you!" So it was time to get serious. "Will you take a dollar," we asked?" "No!" She replied. OK, we said, "How about two dollars," holding them out so she could see them. "But I can't break up the set," she said. "Three dollars, will you take three dollars, PLEASE!!!!" She smiled and took the money. I think the tears is what got her.

PRICE GUIDE

DESCRIPTION		CURRENT PRICES
CUP	- 8 oz.	— $3.00
SAUCER	- 5 ¾"	— 2.00
PLATE, SALAD	- 7 ¾"	— 4.00
PLATE, DINNER	- 9 1/8"	— 6.00
PLATTER, OVAL	- 9"x 12"	— 10.00
BOWL, DESSERT	- 4 7/8"	— 3.50
BOWL, CEREAL	- 5 7/8"	— 4.00
BOWL, SOUP	- 7 5/8"	— 5.00
BOWL, VEGETABLE	- 8 ¼"	— 10.00
SUGAR, LID*	-	— 5.00
CREAMER	-	— 5.00

*Sugar without lid deduct $2.00.

"JADE-ITE SWIRL"
(1949-1951)
G4100

This set of tableware is made from the 4100 line molds, or "Swirl" pattern as it is more commonly called by collectors. There is however, some confusion between the "Swirl" (4100) and the "Shell" (2300) lines. The main differences are as follows: (1) The 4100 line was first made in 1950, where as the 2300 line did not come out till 1963. (2) The "Shell" (2300) line, though very similar to the "Swirl" (4100) line, has one major difference, the 2300 line has a scalloped edge. The 4100 does not.

The trademarks on this pattern are as follows; (OVEN Fire-King GLASS) or (OVEN Fire-King WARE). And as always you will find them on the bottom of each item.

As for the hard to locate pieces of "Jade-ite Swirl", it seems almost everything except a cup and saucer have been impossible to find. If you have any of the other pieces to this set, please let us know. We are willing to buy or beg, if need be, to complete this set.

PRICE GUIDE

DESCRIPTION		CURRENT PRICES
CUP	- 8 oz.	— $4.00
SAUCER	- 5 ¾"	— 2.00
PLATE, SALAD	- 7 ¾"	— 5.00
PLATE, DINNER	- 9 1/8"	— 8.00
PLATTER, OVAL	- 9"x 12"	— 15.00
BOWL, DESSERT	- 4 7/8"	— 5.00
BOWL, CEREAL	- 5 7/8"	— 6.00
BOWL, SOUP	- 7 5/8"	— 8.00
BOWL, VEGETABLE	- 8 ¼"	— 12.00
SUGAR, LID*	-	— 7.00
CREAMER	-	— 7.00

*Sugar without lid deduct $2.00.

"PINK ANCHORGLASS DINNERWARE"
(PINK SWIRL)
(1955-1956)
M4100

The "Pink Dinnerware" came out in the mid 50's as an answer to the everything pink fad so popular about that time, from pink Cadillacs to pink "peddle pushers". Why not pink dinnerware! When found in new condition, "Pink Swirl" is a very attractive pattern to collect.

The "Pink Dinnerware" was made using the 4100 line castings with a fired-on pink color. This color does however, have a tendency to fade, due to heavy use or exposure to strong cleaners. Finding mint pieces is a bit of a challenge. This is the only 4100 pattern to use the 11" serving plate instead of the 9"x12" oval platter. The hard to find pieces are the 7 5/8" soup plate, and the 7¼" vegetable bowls.

The trademark used on this pattern is, (OVEN Fire-King WARE MADE IN U.S.A.), some pieces will have a mold or casting number stamped between the WARE and MADE IN U.S.A. of the trademark.

PRICE GUIDE

DESCRIPTION		CURRENT PRICES
CUP	- 8 oz.	— $3.00
SAUCER	- 5 ¾"	— 2.00
PLATE, SALAD	- 7 ¾"	— 4.00
PLATE, DINNER	- 9 1/8"	— 6.00
PLATTER, SERVING	- 11"	— 10.00
BOWL, DESSERT	- 4 7/8"	— 3.50
BOWL, SOUP	- 7 5/8"	— 6.00
BOWL, VEGETABLE	- 7 ¼"	— 15.00
BOWL, VEGETABLE	- 8 ¼"	— 10.00
SUGAR, LID*	-	— 6.00
CREAMER	-	— 5.00

*Sugar without lid deduct $2.00.

"WHITE SWIRL"
(1959-1962)
W4100

The "White Swirl" pattern has been one of the hardest 4100 dinnerware sets to find all the pieces common to this series. As of this writing, we have found a 4 place setting, (4 cups, 4 saucers, 4 dinner plates, a soup bowl, and a sugar). You must be very careful with this pattern in regard to its color. The "Ivory Swirl" has some very light colored pieces that are very close to the color of the "White Swirl".

The hard to locate pieces seem to be bowls, salad plates, the platter, sugar and creamer. We have failed to find any pieces with the labels still on them. The reason for the small number of pieces being found could be due to several things. One, it could have had a very short series run at the factory. Two, it may have been a pattern, that saw a lot of use in the home. What ever the reason, it's out there somewhere so we'll just keep looking.

The only marking found on this pattern so far is (OVEN Fire-King WARE MADE IN U.S.A.), with most having a mold number under the WARE of the trademark).

PRICE GUIDE		
DESCRIPTION		**CURRENT PRICES**
CUP	- 8 oz.	— $3.00
SAUCER	- 5 ¾"	— 2.00
PLATE, SALAD	- 7 ¾"	— 4.00
PLATE, DINNER	- 9 1/8"	— 6.00
PLATTER, OVAL	- 9"x 12"	— 10.00
BOWL, DESSERT	- 4 7/8"	— 3.50
BOWL, SOUP	- 7 5/8"	— 5.00
BOWL, VEGETABLE	- 8 ¼"	— 10.00
SUGAR, FOOTED	- Open	— 5.00
CREAMER	-	— 5.00

PINK Anchorglass® DINNERWARE

M4179 — M4129

M4174

M4138 — M4141 — M4146

M4167

PACKING

M4179—	8 oz.	Cup	6 doz. —	25 lbs.
M4129—	5¾"	Saucer	6 doz. —	32 lbs.
M4174—	4⅞"	Dessert	6 doz. —	25 lbs.
M4138—	7¾"	Salad Plate	3 doz. —	27 lbs.
M4141—	9⅛"	Dinner Plate	3 doz. —	38 lbs.
M4146—	11"	Serving Plate	1 doz. —	20 lbs.
M4167—	7⅝"	Soup Plate	3 doz. —	29 lbs.

DESIGNED FOR BEAUTY — PRICED FOR EVERYDAY VOLUME SALES.

M4177 — M4178

M4143 — M4144

M4177—	7¼"	Vegetable Bowl	1 doz. — 11 lbs.
M4178—	8¼"	Vegetable Bowl	1 doz. — 15 lbs.
M4143—		Sugar & Cover	2 doz. — 11 lbs.
M4144—		Creamer	2 doz. — 12 lbs.

Each Piece comes with a beautiful Pink, Black and Gold
label reading "PINK HEAT-PROOF ANCHORGLASS."

See Listing of Prepacked Sets on Page 2.

— HEAT-PROOF —

10.

IVORY *Fire-King* TABLEWARE

★ W4179 — ★ W4129

★ W4174

★ W4138 — ★ W4141

W4167

			COST DOZ.	PACKING
★ W4179—	Cup		.47	6 doz. — 26 lbs.
★ W4129—	Saucer		.47	6 doz. — 30 lbs.
★ W4174—4 ⅞″	Dessert		.47	6 doz. — 24 lbs.
★ W4138—7 ¾″	Salad Plate		.95	3 doz. — 24 lbs.
★ W4141—9 ⅛″	Dinner Plate		1.25	3 doz. — 38 lbs.
W4167—7 ⅝″	Soup Plate		.95	3 doz. — 29 lbs.

W4147

★ W4178

W4153 — W4154

		COST	PACKING
W4147—12″x9″	Platter	1.77	1 doz. — 21 lbs.
★ W4178—8 ¼″	Vegetable Bowl	1.65	1 doz. — 15 lbs.
W4153—	Sugar & Cover	.95	3 doz. — 21 lbs.
W4154—	Creamer	.65	3 doz. — 17 lbs.

★ W4100/20

W4100/49

★ W4100/20—12 Pce. Starter Set ..... (Each Set in Gift Ctn.) ...... .80 Set   6 Sets — 47 lbs.
    COMP.: Four Each Cups, Saucers and Dinner Plates
W4100/49—20 Pce. Dinner Set ..... (Each Set in Gift Ctn.) 1.18 Set   4 Sets — 52 lbs.
    COMP.: Four Each Cups, Saucers, Desserts,
            Salad Plates and Dinner Plates.

*Reg. U. S. Pat. Off.

24.   **Listing with ANCHOR HOCKING GLASS CORP., Lancaster, Ohio, U. S. A.**   *PRINTED IN U.S.A.*

ANCHORWHITE DINNERWARE — HEAT-PROOF

W4179 — W4129

W4174

W4138 — W4141

W4167

			PACKING
W4179—	Cup		6 doz. — 26 lbs.
W4129—	Saucer		6 doz. — 28 lbs.
W4174—4⅞″	Dessert		6 doz. — 24 lbs.
W4138—7¾″	Salad Plate		3 doz. — 26 lbs.
W4141—9⅛″	Dinner Plate		3 doz. — 37 lbs.
W4167—7⅝″	Soup Plate		3 doz. — 31 lbs.

W4178

W4147

W4153 — W4154

W4178— 8¼″	Vegetable Bowl		1 doz. — 15 lbs.
W4147—12 x 9″	Platter		1 doz. — 21 lbs.
W4153—	Sugar		2 doz. — 10 lbs.
W4154—	Creamer		2 doz. — 10 lbs.

MISCELLANEOUS

W383 — W327

W384 — W327

W341

W383—8 oz.	Ransom Cup		4 doz. — 20 lbs.
W327—5⅞″	Saucer		4 doz. — 19 lbs.
W384—9 oz.	St. Denis Cup		4 doz. — 22 lbs.
W327—5⅞″	Saucer		4 doz. — 19 lbs.
W341—9⅛″	Dinner Plate		3 doz. — 39 lbs.

HEAT-PROOF

Clockwise, Left to Right: Splash Proof Mixing Bowl Set, Oval Relish, Egg Plate, Swedish Modern (teardrop) Mixing Bowls, Various Sizes of Ashtrays, Snack Set, **(Center)** 5″ Basketweave Bowl.

"TURQUOISE BLUE" DINNERWARE
(1956-1959)
B4000

"Turquoise Blue" seems to be one of the most treasured patterns of Anchor Hocking's "FIRE-KING" dinnerware to be collected. As usual in most blue glassware, it is the most popular, and therefore quickly becomes the hardest to find. Some items such as the 10" plates, the 7¼" salad, the 6¼" bread and butter, and all the bowls are already hard to find. The 9" plate, the creamer, sugar, and the cup and saucer are found most often.

There are several items of "Turquoise Blue" trimmed in 22K Gold. These consist of the relish dish, egg tray, and snack set. The snack set came packed in a box of four cups and four 9" plates, which had an indent for the cup. Placing these items in the microwave could damage or remove the gold trim. All items in "Turquoise Blue", except for the egg tray, are embossed (OVEN Fire-King WARE MADE IN U.S.A.).

"Turquoise Blue" has become a favorite pattern for us to collect. We are still trying to add more pieces to our collection. So if you're interested in collecting this pattern, get up before daylight, find a nice country restaurant for breakfast, and look ahead for us, because we started 30 minutes earlier!

PRICE GUIDE

DESCRIPTION		CURRENT PRICES
CUP	- 8 oz.	— $3.00
SAUCER	- 5¾"	— 2.00
PLATE, BREAD & BUTTER	- 6¼"	— 4.00
PLATE, SALAD	- 7 ¼"	— 6.00
PLATE, DINNER	- 9"	— 7.00
PLATE, SERVING	- 10"	— 20.00
BOWL, DESSERT	- 4 5/8"	— 4.00
BOWL, CEREAL	- 5"	— 5.00
BOWL, SOUP	- 6 5/8"	— 15.00
BOWL, VEGETABLE	- 8¼"	— 10.00
SUGAR, OPEN	- 8¼"	— 4.50
CREAMER	-	— 4.50
MUG	-	— 8.00

"TURQUOISE BLUE" DINNERWARE
(1956-1959)
B4000

PARTY WARE

PRICE GUIDE

DESCRIPTION		CURRENT PRICES
EGG PLATE	- 22K Gold Trimmed Edge	— $15.00
RELISH PLATE, Oval	- 22K Gold Trimmed Edge	— 10.00
SNACK PLATE	- 22K Gold Trimmed Edge	— 6.00
SNACK CUP	- 22K Gold Trimmed Edge	— 3.50
ASH TRAY	- 3½"	— 4.00
ASH TRAY	- 4 5/8"	— 7.00
ASH TRAY	- 5¾"	— 10.00
BOWL, Basket Weave	- 4¾"	— 15.00
SNACK SET In The Box	- 8 Pc.	— 35.00
(4 Cups, 4 Plates)		

For Price of Mixing Bowls see page 108.

TURQUOISE-BLUE TABLEWARE — HEAT-PROOF

B4079 — B4029

B4074

B4037 — B4038 — B4041 — B4046

PACKING

B4079—	8 oz.	Cup	6 doz. — 24 lbs.
B4029—	5¾"	Saucer	6 doz. — 32 lbs.
B4074—	4⅝"	Dessert	6 doz. — 23 lbs.
B4037—	6¼"	Bread & Butter Plate	3 doz. — 18 lbs.
B4038—	7¼"	Salad Plate	3 doz. — 23 lbs.
B4041—	9"	Dinner Plate	3 doz. — 42 lbs.
B4046—	10"	Serving Plate	1 doz. — 18 lbs.

See Mixing Bowls on Page 27, Mug and Bowl on Page 23 and Ash Trays on Page 41.

B4067

B4078

B4053 — B4054

B4067—	6⅝"	Soup Plate	3 doz. — 26 lbs.
B4078—	8¼"	Vegetable Bowl	1 doz. — 17 lbs.
B4053—		Sugar	2 doz. — 11 lbs.
B4054—		Creamer	2 doz. — 11 lbs.

B4000/18

PREPACKED SETS

B4000/18—12 Pce. Starter Set
Each Set in Display Style Carton, 6 Sets to Shipper — 48 lbs.
COMPOSITION: Four Each B4079 Cups, B4029 Saucers and B4041 Dinner Plates

B4000/19—18 Pce. Luncheon Set
Each Set in Gift Carton, 4 Sets to Shipper — 40 lbs.
COMPOSITION: Four Each B4079 Cups, B4029 Saucers, B4074 Desserts, and B4041 Dinner Plates; One Each B4053 Sugar and B4054 Creamer

B4000/21—34 Pce. Dinner Set
Each Set in Shipping Carton — 20 lbs.
COMPOSITION: Six Each B4079 Cups, B4029 Saucers, B4074 Desserts, B4038 Salad Plates and B4041 Dinner Plates; One Each B4078 Vegetable Bowl, B4046 Serving Plate, B4053 Sugar and B4054 Creamer

B4000/22—52 Pce. Dinner Set
Each Set in Shipping Carton — 32 lbs.
COMPOSITION: Eight Each B4079 Cups, B4029 Saucers, B4074 Desserts, B4038 Salad Plates, B4067 Soup Plates and B4041 Dinner Plates; One Each B4078 Vegetable Bowl, B4046 Serving Plate, B4053 Sugar and B4054 Creamer

18

TURQUOISE-BLUE MIXING BOWL SETS

NEW SWEDISH MODERN SHAPE

B500/39—4 Pce. Mixing Bowl Set
   Each Set in Gift Carton, 4 Sets to Shipping Carton — 31½ lbs.
COMPOSITION: One 1 Pt. Mixing Bowl
                One 1 Qt. Mixing Bowl
                One 2 Qt. Mixing Bowl
                One 3 Qt. Mixing Bowl

B500/40—3 Pce. Mixing Bowl Set
   Each Set in Gift Carton, 4 Sets to Shipping Carton — 19 lbs.
COMPOSITION: One 1 Pt. Mixing Bowl
                One 1 Qt. Mixing Bowl
                One 2 Qt. Mixing Bowl

SPLASH-PROOF SHAPE

B300/213—3 Pce. Mixing Bowl Set
   2 Dozen Sets Bulk Packed in 4 Cartons — 127 lbs.

B300/214—3 Pce. Mixing Bowl Set
   Each Set Nested and Packed in an Individual
   Cell — 8 Sets to Shipping Carton — 40 lbs.

The Sets listed above consist of one each of the
B366, B367 and B368 Bowls.

OPEN STOCK   PACKING
B366—1 Qt. Mixing Bowl   2 doz. — 28 lbs.
B367—2 Qt. Mixing Bowl   2 doz. — 43 lbs.
B368—3 Qt. Mixing Bowl   1 doz. — 28 lbs.

1957-1958 Anchor Hocking Catalog

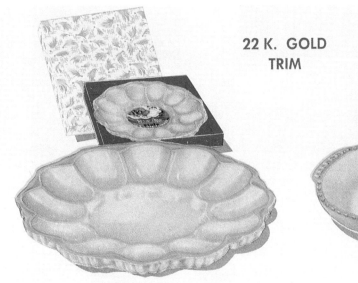

22 K. GOLD TRIM

B896-G/13

B50-G/13

B896-G/13— 9¾" Egg Plate .... 1 doz. — 24 lbs.
B50-G/13—11⅛" Divided Relish .... 1 doz. — 24 lbs.

EACH OF THE ABOVE ITEMS PACKS IN AN INDIVIDUAL DISPLAY BOX AS ILLUSTRATED.

More Gift-Boxed Ware is shown on Page 30.

28.

79

"WHEAT" DINNERWARE
(1962-1966)
W4600/65

Production of this pattern began in the latter part of 1961, and continued through the late 60's. This is one of the most popular patterns of the W4600 series dinnerware castings. "Wheat" also had an 11 piece set of ovenware which most other patterns of "FIRE-KING" did not have. The casseroles could be bought with candlewarmers that boasted "lustrous brass finish and genuine walnut handles on each end". There was also a snack set that consisted of 4 rectangular trays and four 5 oz. cups.

"Wheat" was made in a milk white color with a bright golden cluster of wheat fired on to each piece of dinnerware. The ovenware has a mirror image cluster of wheat on both sides of each item. The casseroles came with clear glass cover.

The markings you will find are, (OVEN Fire-King WARE MADE IN U.S.A.) or (ANCHOR HOCKING OVEN Fire-King WARE MAKE IN U.S.A.). Please note this is the first pattern of "FIRE-KING" to be marked "ANCHOR HOCKING". All other patterns after 1962 are marked "ANCHOR HOCKING". On some of the dinnerware and ovenware pieces you will find a number located between "FIRE-KING" and MADE IN U.S.A. This number was used by Anchor Hocking to identify the mold used to cast each piece of glass just in case a flaw was found. The number you find at the top of the trademark on the ovenware, is used to identify the piece, and also to match the cover to its proper piece. The number on the cover is located on the outer edge. This sure helps when your looking through a box full of covers for the one that fits the casserole dish you have at home.

PRICE GUIDE		
DESCRIPTION		CURRENT PRICES
CUP	- 8 oz.	— $3.00
SAUCER	- 5¾"	— 1.00
PLATE, BREAD & BUTTER	- 6¼"	— 2.00
PLATE, SALAD	- 7 3/8"	— 3.00
PLATE, DINNER	- 10"	— 5.00
PLATTER, OVAL	- 9" x 12"	— 6.00
BOWL, DESSERT	- 4 5/8"	— 3.00

PRICE GUIDE		
DESCRIPTION		CURRENT PRICES
BOWL, SOUP	- 6 5/8"	— $6.00
BOWL, VEGETABLE	- 8¼"	— 6.00
SUGAR & LID *	-	— 4.00
CREAMER	-	— 3.00
PLATE, SNACK SET	- 6"x11"	— 3.00
CUP, SNACK SET	- 5 oz.	— 1.50

*Sugar Without Lid Deduct $1.00

"WHEAT"
OVENWARE

PRICE GUIDE		
DESCRIPTION		CURRENT PRICE
DESSERT	- 6 oz.	— $3.00
CASSEROLE, Lid	- 1 pt.	— 4.00
CASSEROLE, Lid	- 1 qt.	— 5.00
CASSEROLE, Lid	- 1½ qt.	— 6.00
CASSEROLE, Lid	- 1½ qt. (Oval)	— 7.00
CASSEROLE, Lid	- 2 qt.	— 7.00
CAKE PAN, Round	- 8"	— 5.00
CAKE PAN, Square	- 8"	— 5.00
PAN, DEEP LOAF, Lid	- 5"X9"	— 6.00
PAN, UTILITY BAKING	- 6½"X10½"	— 5.00
PAN, UTILITY BAKING	- 8"X12½"	— 6.00

wheat dinnerware

Heat-resistant; golden wheat on a clean contemporary shape.
Matches Wheat ovenware. In open stock and packaged sets.

			Doz. Ctn.	Lbs. Ctn.
W4679/65	8 oz	cup	3	14
W4629/65	5¾"	saucer	3	14
W4674/65	4⅝"	dessert	3	11
W4638/65	7⅜"	salad plate	3	23
W4667/65	6⅝"	soup plate	3	25
W4646/65	10"	dinner plate	3	44
W4678/65	8¼"	vegetable bowl	1	14
W4647/65	12 x 9"	platter	1	20
W4653/65		sugar/cover	1	9
W4654/65		creamer	1	7

Packed Sets

		Sets Ctn.	Lbs. Ctn.
W4600/46	16 pc set, display carton, 4 cups, 4 saucers, 4 desserts, 4 dinner plates	4	38
W4600/47	35 pc set, 6 cups, 6 saucers, 6 desserts, 6 soup plates, 6 dinner plates, vegetable, platter, sugar/cover, creamer	1	23
W4600/48	53 pc set, 8 cups, 8 saucers, 8 desserts, 8 salad plates, 8 soup plates, 8 dinner plates, vegetable, platter, sugar/cover, creamer	1	34

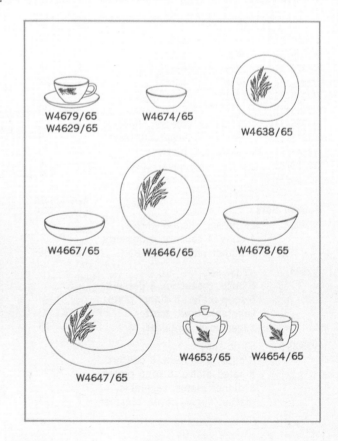

W4679/65
W4629/65

W4674/65

W4638/65

W4667/65

W4646/65

W4678/65

W4647/65

W4653/65

W4654/65

36

Wheat Anchorwhite Ovenware

W424/65

W405/65 — W406/65

W407/65 — W408/65

PACKING

W424/65—6	oz. Dessert or Low Custard	4 doz. — 14 lbs.
W405/65—1	Pt. Casserole—Knob Cover	1 doz. — 16 lbs.
W406/65—1	Qt. Casserole—Knob Cover	½ doz. — 14 lbs.
W407/65—1 ½	Qt. Casserole—Knob Cover	½ doz. — 19 lbs.
W408/65—2	Qt. Casserole—Knob Cover	½ doz. — 22 lbs.

All Covers are Clear Crystal Fire-King.

W467/65

W450/65

W452/65

W467/65—1 ½	Qt. Casserole—Au Gratin Cover	½ doz. — 18 lbs.
W450/65—8"	Round Cake Pan	½ doz. — 12 lbs.
W452/65—8"	Square Cake Pan	½ doz. — 17 lbs.

GUARANTEED 2 YEARS AGAINST OVEN BREAKAGE.

To be replaced Free by dealer in exchange for broken pieces.

W409/65

W410/65 — W411/65

W409/65—5 x 9"	Deep Loaf Pan	½ doz. — 12 lbs.
W410/65—6 ½ x 10 ½"	Utility Baking Pan	½ doz. — 15 lbs.
W411/65—8 x 12 ½"	Utility Baking Pan	½ doz. — 22 lbs.

**"Fire-King" — The World's Finest Baking Ware. Also available
in Crystal, Anchorwhite and Copper-Tint.**

54.

□□

"THREE BANDS"
(1950's)

Due to the fact we have not been able to find this pattern listed in any Anchor Hocking catalog, or magazine ad, and also due to Anchor Hocking not having kept records on all of it's premium lines, we have given this line the name "Three Bands". Three deeply embossed bands encircle each piece. These bands have a little dip in their design as they move around the piece. We have found pieces of this pattern in the colors of jade-ite, ivory, and lustre. The most common being the lustre cup and saucer. We also have four ivory dinner plates and a jade-ite vegetable bowl. This leads us to believe tableware set's were made in the ivory and jade-ite colors. Due to the abundance of the lustre cups and saucers, these were used as premiums. What company used these, or what other pieces were available we do not know. Maybe some of you collectors can tell us.

The trademark found on these pieces are, (OVEN Fire-King WARE MADE IN U.S.A.). This trademark helps date this pattern to the early to mid 50's.

The hard to find pieces are everything, with the exception of the lustre cup and saucer.

PRICE GUIDE

DESCRIPTION		CURRENT PRICES		
		JADE-ITE	IVORY	LUSTRE
CUP	- 8 oz.	— $5.00	— $4.00	— $3.00
SAUCER	- 5¾"	— 2.00	— 2.00	— 1.00
PLATE, SALAD	- 7 ¾"	— 5.00	— 4.00	— 3.00
PLATE, DINNER	- 9 ¼"	— 8.00	— 6.00	— 5.00
PLATTER, OVAL	- 9"x12"	— 10.00	— 8.00	— 7.00
BOWL, DESSERT	- 4 7/8"	— 4.00	— 4.00	— 3.00
BOWL, SOUP	- 7 ½"	— 8.00	— 6.00	— 5.00
BOWL, VEGETABLE	- 8 ¼"	— 10.00	— 8.00	— 6.00
SUGAR	-	— 6.00	— 5.00	— 4.00
CREAMER	-	— 6.00	— 5.00	— 4.00

"PREMIUM CUP & SAUCER SETS"
(1960'S)

Here again is a mystery waiting to be solved. These cup and saucer sets don't seem to have matching plates and bowls needed to make a tableware setting. So we must assume these cup and saucer sets were given away as premiums. We have not found them listed in any Anchor Hocking catalog or sales ad.

There are five different cup and saucer sets, each set having a different floral design, (1) red and yellow tulips, (2) a pair of red roses, (3) red and yellow pansies, (4) blue asters, and (5) blue flowers and tiny red berries. There are also two slightly different styles of cups. One is just a little shorter than the other. We have found a few saucers to have two floral designs on them instead of the usual one design.

The trademarks found on these sets are, (OVEN Fire-King WARE, mold #, MADE IN U.S.A.), or (Anchor Hocking [anchor over H symbol] Fire-King WARE MADE IN U.S.A.).

These sets are very plentiful in our region. With almost every yard sale having at least one or more of the cups or saucers for sale.

PRICE GUIDE

DESCRIPTION		CURRENT PRICES
CUP, (All Floral Designs)	- 8 oz.	— $3.00
SAUCER, (All Floral Designs)	- 5 ¾"	— 1.00

Top Row: Swirl Bowls, 1½ qt. Swirl Casserole. **Row 2:** French (smooth) Casserole, 9″ Pie Plate, 5″ Bowl, 6 oz. Dessert, Ribbed French Casserole. **Row 3:** Round Cake Pan 8″, 1½ qt. Oval Casserole, Oval Divided Dish. **Row 4:** 8″ Square Cake Pan, 6½″x10½″ Utility Baking Pan, 5″x9″ Deep Dish Baking Pan.

Top Row: 9″ Pie Plate, Round Swirl Bowl, 1½ qt. Casserole, 1 qt. Casserole, 8″ Round Cake Pan. **Row 2:** 1½ qt. Oval Casserole, 6 oz. Dessert, 6½″x10½″ Utility Pan, 6 oz. Dessert (swirl), 5″x9″ Deep Loaf Pan. **Row 3:** Mixing Bowl, 4 5/8″ (swirl) Cereal, 10 oz. Covered Casserole, 11¾″ Divided Oval Dish, 2 qt. Casserole.

"ANCHORWHITE OVENWARE"
(1959-1964)
W400

The "Anchorwhite Ovenware" has held up very well over the years. The pieces we have found of this pattern are in excellent condition despite heavy use. This is the ovenware we use for everyday oven, or microwave cooking. After each use, we just throw it in the dishwasher, and it comes out shining like new. This pattern, like all the rest of the ovenware, has an item number that matches the number found on the lid. This makes it much easier to find the right lid, when you are digging through those boxes of lids you find under counters at flea markets and antique shops.

For trademark information please refer to "Crystal Ovenware" as the trademark and item numbers are the same.

The hard to find and unusual pieces are 1 qt. and 2 qt. casseroles, the ribbed French casserole with glass lid, and the large footed well and tree platter. NOTE: The French casseroles do not have item numbers, and come in two styles; ribbed and smooth sided. The latter came with plastic lids.

PRICE GUIDE

DESCRIPTION		CURRENT PRICES
CASSEROLE, Knob Cover	- 1 pt.	— $4.50
CASSEROLE, Knob Cover	- 1 qt.	— 5.00
CASSEROLE, Knob Cover	- 1½ qt.	— 6.00
CASSEROLE, Knob Cover	- 2 qt.	— 7.00
CASSEROLE, SWIRL, Knob Cover	- 1½ qt.	— 7.00
CASSEROLE, OVAL, Au Gratin Lid	- 1½ qt.	— 6.00
CASSEROLE, FRENCH, Rib, c/lid	- 12 oz.	— 5.00
DESSERT	- 6 oz.	— 3.00
CAKE PAN, ROUND	- 8"	— 6.00
CAKE PAN, SQUARE	- 8"	— 6.00
PAN, DEEP LOAF	- 5" x 9"	— 5.00

PRICE GUIDE

DESCRIPTION		CURRENT PRICES
PAN, PIE	- 9"	— $4.00
PAN, PIE	- 10"	— 5.00
PAN, BAKING, Utility	- 6½" x 10½"	— 6.00
PAN, BAKING, Utility	- 8" x 12½"	— 8.00
PAN, BAKING, Cover	- 5" x 9"	— 7.00
DISH, OVAL, Divided	- 11¾"	— 6.00
PLATTER, Footed, Well & Tree	- 14¾"x10 7/8"	— 15.00
CASSEROLE, FRENCH, s/s, pl/lid	- 12 oz.	— 3.00
CASSEROLE FRENCH, Rib., gl/lid	- 12 oz.	— 5.00
BOWL	- 5"	— 3.00

(Without lid deduct $1.00)

"COPPER-TINT OVENWARE"
(1958-1971)
L400

The "Copper-Tint" or lustre color finish used on this set of ovenware has brightened up many a kitchen in its time. It seems that almost everyone who set up housekeeping in the 50's and 60's have a few pieces of this ovenware. It was a very popular wedding gift. Back in the days before microwave cooking, it saw quite a lot of use. The only flaw was the copper-tint finish was a little sensitive to strong cleaners, and scratched rather easily.

For trademarks refer to the "Crystal Ovenware". You will find that item numbers are the same for each piece no matter what pattern you have. The labels read; (Fire-King COPPER TINT OVENWARE two year guarantee against oven breakage, (good housekeeping seal of approval) Anchor Hocking Glass Corp. Lancaster Ohio U.S.A.).

The hard to find pieces are 1 qt. and 2 qt. casseroles, 8"x12½" utility pan and the lid for the deep loaf pan. Also due to it's sensitive finish it will be hard finding this pattern in mint condition. We have however, been able to find a few pieces of this set with the original labels.

PRICE GUIDE

DESCRIPTION		CURRENT PRICES
CASSEROLE, Knob Cover	- 1 pt.	— $4.50
CASSEROLE, Knob Cover	- 1 qt.	— 5.00
CASSEROLE, Knob Cover	- 1½ qt.	— 6.00
CASSEROLE, Knob Cover	- 2 qt.	— 7.00
CASSEROLE, OVAL, Au Gratin Lid	- 1 ½ qt.	— 6.00
CASSEROLE, FRENCH, Tab Lid	- 12 oz.	— 5.00
DESSERT	- 6 oz.	— 3.00
CAKE PAN, ROUND	- 8"	— 6.00
CAKE PAN, SQUARE	- 8"	— 6.00

PRICE GUIDE

DESCRIPTION		CURRENT PRICES
PAN, DEEP LOAF	- 5"x9"	— $5.00
PAN, PIE	- 9"	— 4.00
PAN, PIE	- 10"	— 5.00
PAN, BAKING, Utility	- 6½"x10½"	— 6.00
PAN, BAKING, Utility	- 8"x12½"	— 8.00
PAN, BAKING, Cover	- 5"x9"	— 7.00
DISH, OVAL, DIVIDED	- 11¾"	— 6.00

(Without lid deduct $1.00)

ANCHORWHITE OVENWARE — GUARANTEED

W424

W405 — W406

W407 — W408

PACKING

W424—6 oz. Dessert or Low Custard		4 doz. — 14 lbs.
W405—1 Pt. Casserole—Knob Cover		1 doz. — 16 lbs.
W406—1 Qt. Casserole—Knob Cover		½ doz. — 14 lbs.
W407—1½ Qt. Casserole—Knob Cover		½ doz. — 19 lbs.
W408—2 Qt. Casserole—Knob Cover		½ doz. — 22 lbs.

All Covers are Clear Crystal Fire-King.

W235

W467

W468

W235—12 oz. French Casserole & Cover		2 doz. — 28 lbs.
W467— 1½ Qt. Oval Casserole—Au Gratin Cover		½ doz. — 19 lbs.
W468—11¾″ Oval Divided Dish		½ doz. — 14 lbs.

See Prepacked Set on Page 5.

W460 — W462

W450

W452

W460— 9″ Pie Plate		1 doz. — 15 lbs.
W462— 10″ Pie Plate		1 doz. — 21 lbs.
W450— 8″ Round Cake Pan		½ doz. — 12 lbs.
W452— 8″ Square Cake Pan		½ doz. — 17 lbs.

GUARANTEED 2 YEARS AGAINST OVEN BREAKAGE.
To be replaced Free by dealer in exchange for broken pieces.

(Continued on Next Page)

FIRE-KING

HEAT-PROOF

ANCHORWHITE OVENWARE — GUARANTEED

W409

W469

W410 — W411

			PACKING	
W409—5 x 9"	Deep Loaf Pan		½ doz. — 12 lbs.	
W469—5 x 9"	Baking Pan & Cover		½ doz. — 20 lbs.	
W410—6 ½ x 10 ½"	Utility Baking Pan		½ doz. — 15 lbs.	
W411—8 x 12 ½"	Utility Baking Pan		½ doz. — 23 lbs.	

All Covers are Clear Crystal Fire-King.

PREPACKED SET

**12-PCE.
ANCHORWHITE
SET**

**Promote
Prepacked
Sets**

W400/201—12 Pce. Ovenware Set
Each Set in Gift Carton, 4 Sets to Shipping Carton — 57 lbs.
COMPOSITION:
One W407 Casserole—Knob Cover
One W460 Pie Plate
One W409 Deep Loaf Pan
One W410 Utility Baking Pan
One W452 Square Cake Pan
Six W424 Desserts or Low Custards

**GUARANTEED
2 YEARS**

**HEAT
PROOF**

See Pages 2 and 3 for Fire-King "Primrose" Ovenware. Crystal Ovenware is on
Pages 6, 7, 8, and 9 and Ovenware in Copper-Tint on Pages 10 and 11.

L424

L405 — L406

L407 — L408

PACKING

L424—6	oz.	Dessert or Low Custard	4 doz. —	14 lbs.
L405—1	Pt.	Casserole—Knob Cover	1 doz. —	12 lbs.
L406—1	Qt.	Casserole—Knob Cover	½ doz. —	14 lbs.
L407—1 ½	Qt.	Casserole—Knob Cover	½ doz. —	18 lbs.
L408—2	Qt.	Casserole—Knob Cover	½ doz. —	21 lbs.

HEAT-RESISTANT

L467

L450

L452

L467—1 ½	Qt.	Oval Casserole—Au Gratin Cover	½ doz. —	20 lbs.
L450—8″		Round Cake Pan	½ doz. —	11 lbs.
L452—8″		Square Cake Pan	½ doz. —	17 lbs.

All Covers are Clear Crystal Fire-King.

L460

L409

L410 — L411

L460—9″		Pie Plate	1 doz. —	15 lbs.
L409—5 x 9″		Deep Loaf Pan	½ doz. —	11 lbs.
L410—6 ½ x 10 ½″		Utility Baking Pan	½ doz. —	15 lbs.
L411—8 x 12 ½″		Utility Baking Pan	½ doz. —	22 lbs.

GUARANTEED 2 YEARS AGAINST OVEN BREAKAGE.

To be replaced Free by dealer in exchange for broken pieces.

COPPER-TINT FIRE-KING OVENWARE	CARTON		PRICE
	Doz.	Lbs.	Doz.
L436 1 qt. casserole w/knob cover (022723)	½	15	$5.88
L437 1½ qt. casserole w/knob cover (022848)	½	19	7.14
L438 2 qt. casserole w/knob cover (023863)	½	22	8.34
L439 3 qt. casserole w/knob cover (022871)	½	26	11.88
L433 1½ qt. oval casserole w/au gratin cover (022855)	½	21	7.14
L434 6 oz. dessert/low custard (022681)	4	15	1.05
L429 9″ round cake pan (022889)	½	13	5.34
L435 8″ square cake pan (022897)	½	14	5.88
L441 5 x 9″ loaf pan (022905)	½	10	5.88
L432 1½ qt. utility pan (022913)	½	15	5.88
L431 2 qt. utility pan (022921)	½	17	7.74

Good Housekeeping

Replacement Offer: If dish ever breaks from normal oven heat, and instructions have been followed, your dealer will replace it upon being properly notified.

Top Row: 1 qt. Measuring Cup, 16 oz. Measuring Cup, 8 oz. Measuring Cup, 2 qt. Measuring Bowl. **Row 2:** Pie Plate (juice saver), 9" Pie Plate, 8" Pie Plate. **Row 3:** 1.5 oz. Custard, 10 oz. Custard, 6 oz. Custard, 6 oz. Deep Custard, 5 oz. Custard, 6 oz. Smooth Rim Custard, 10 oz. Individual Casserole. **Row 4:** Table Server, Deep Loaf Pan, Utility Pan.

"CRYSTAL OVENWARE"
(1948-1976)
400

"Crystal Clear Ovenware" production began in the late 40's and continues today. Anchor Hocking dropped the "FIRE-KING" trademark in 1976, when they changed their corporate symbol from the anchor over "H" to the anchor within a rounded square. Until this time the trademarks found on the crystal ovenware had changed only once, when in the early 60's they added the name "Anchor Hocking". What we will cover here are the "FIRE-KING" years.

The trademarks are, as you read from top to bottom; (item number, T.M. REG., FIRE-KING, mold number, MADE IN U.S.A., size). EXAMPLE: The 10 oz. deep pie dish trademarks read like this; (425, T.M. REG., FIRE-KING, 3, MADE IN U.S.A., 10 oz.). The mold number can be any number from 1-40 according to the number of molds to the machine. The older trademark of the measuring cups read; (item number, T.M. REG., FIRE-KING, mold number, MADE IN U.S.A. size, GRADUATED FOR COOKING USE ONLY). Also some of the trademarks are read from the bottom while others are read from the inside. The Anchor Hocking marked pieces read like this; (item number, ANCHOR HOCKING, [anchor over H symbol], Fire-King, OVEN-PROOF, mold number, MADE IN U.S.A., size).

There are two early styles of covers. First was the raised knob lid, similar to the lids used on the "Sapphire Blue" ovenware. Second was the flat top lid with an etched circle. On every lid you will find a number that matches the lid with it's mates.

PRICE GUIDE				PRICE GUIDE		
DESCRIPTION		CURRENT PRICES		DESCRIPTION		CURRENT PRICES
CASSEROLE, INDIVIDUAL, Lid	- 10 oz.	— $3.00		PAN, PIE, DEEP (Juice Saver)	- 9"	— $8.00
CASSEROLE, Knob Cover	- 1 pt.	— 4.50		PAN, PIE	- 10"	— 6.00
CASSEROLE, Knob Cover	- 1 qt.	— 5.00		PAN, BAKING, Utility	- 8' x 12½"	— 6.00
CASSEROLE, Knob Cover	- 1 ½ qt.	— 6.00		PAN, BAKING, Utility	- 6¼" x 7¼"	— 5.00
CASSEROLE, Knob Cover	- 2 qt.	— 7.00		MEASURING CUP, Red/Line	- 8 oz.	— 3.00
CASSEROLE, Oval Knob Cover	- 1 ½"	— 4.50		MEASURING CUP, Red/Line	- 16 oz.	— 4.00
CASSEROLE, FRENCH, Tab Lid	- 12 oz.	— 5.00		MEASURING CUP, Red/Line	- 1 qt.	— 5.00
CUSTARD, STD.	- 5 oz.	— 3.00		MEASURING BOWL,	- 2 qt.	— 6.00
CUSTARD, DEEP	- 6 oz.	— 2.00		PUDDING PAN	- 1 qt.	— 3.00
CUSTARD, DESSERT	- 6 oz.	— 2.00		TABLE SERVER	-	— 10.00
CUSTARD, DEEP PIE DISH	- 10 oz.	— 3.00		PERCOLATOR, TOP	-	— 2.00
CUSTARD, DEEP PIE DISH	- 15 oz.	— 3.50		PAN, BAKING	- 6½" x 10½"	— 4.00
CAKE PAN, SQUARE	- 8"	— 6.00		BAKER, (No Lid)	- 1 qt.	— 3.00
PAN, DEEP LOAF	- 5" x 9"	— 5.00		BAKER, (No Lid)	- 1 ½ qt.	— 4.00
PAN, PIE	- 8"	— 3.00		BAKER, (No Lid)	- 2 qt.	— 5.00
PAN, PIE	- 9"	— 4.00				

422—5 oz. Standard Custard
6 doz. — 18 lbs.

423—6 oz. Egg Cup & Deep Custard
6 doz. — 22 lbs.

424—6 oz. Dessert or Low Custard
6 doz. — 22 lbs.

425—10 o

496—8 oz. Measuring Cup—
Red Graduations
2 doz. — 13 lbs.

498—16 oz. Measuring Pitcher—
Red Graduations
1 doz. — 13 lbs.

499—1 Qt. Measuring Pitcher—
Red Graduations
1 doz. — 24 lbs.

459—8" P

460—9" P

405—1 Pt. Casserole—Knob Cover
2 doz. — 33 lbs.

406—1 Qt. Casserole—Knob Cover
1 doz. — 30 lbs.

407—1½ Qt. Casserole—Knob Cover
1 doz. — 35 lbs.

408—2 Qt. Casserole—Knob Cover
1 doz. — 41 lbs.

THE WO
BAK

GUARANTEED 2 YEA

To be replaced Free by d

See Prepa

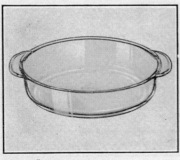

450—8" Round Cake Pan
1 doz. — 22 lbs.

452—8" Square Cake Pan
1 doz. — 34 lbs.

409—5 x 9" Deep Loaf Pan
1 doz. — 22 lbs.

440—6¼ x

20.

426—15 oz. Deep Pie Dish
4 doz. — 30 lbs.

442—8 oz. Individual Baker
4 doz. — 21 lbs.

435—2⅛" Percolator Top
6 doz. — 12 lbs.

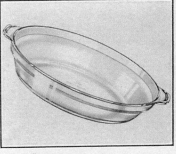

461—9" Deep Pie Plate
1 doz. — 19 lbs.

443—1 Qt. Pudding Pan
2 doz. — 27 lbs.

402—8 oz. Individual Casserole & Cover
3 doz. — 28 lbs.

FINEST
WARE

T OVEN BREAKAGE.

hange for broken pieces.

Page 22.

497—1½ Qt. Casserole—Utility Cover
1 doz. — 36 lbs.

446—1 Qt. Baker—No Cover
1 doz. — 16 lbs.

447—1½ Qt. Baker—No Cover
1 doz. — 20 lbs.

448—2 Qt. Baker—No Cover
1 doz. — 24 lbs.

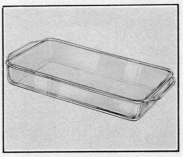

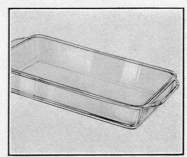

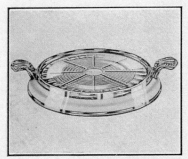

ing Pan

410—6½ x 10½" Utility Baking Pan
1 doz. — 30 lbs.

411—8 x 12½" Utility Baking Pan
1 doz. — 40 lbs.

451—Table Server
1 doz. — 15 lbs.

21.

Top Row: 8½" Colonial Bowl, 6" Colonial Bowl. **Row 2:** 4¼"x8¼" Refrigerator Jar, 4⅛"x4⅛" Refrigerator Jars, 1½ qt. Oval Casserole. **Row 3:** 8" Round Cake Pan, 6½x10½ Utility Pan, Colonial Batter Bowl.

Top Row: 6 oz. Custard, Refrigerator Dish, Large Refrigerator Dish, Refrigerator Dish, Mug. **Row 2:** 3 6-oz. Custards, 1 pt. Casserole, 6½x10½ Utility Pan. **Row 3:** Colonial Batter Bowl, 6" Colonial Mixing Bowl, 5" Cereal Bowl, 6" Colonial Mixing Bowl. **Row 4:** 6¼x10½ Refrigerator Dish, 2 4⅛x4⅛ Refrigerator Bowls, 2 French Casserole.

HAND PAINTED "ANCHORWHITE" FIRE-KING
(1957-1964)

During the late 50's the mid 60's the Gay Fad Studio's (Lancaster, Ohio) made very large orders of Anchorwhite mugs, 5" cereal bowls, refrigerator jar sets, mixing bowl sets, batter bowls, and ovenware sets. They hand painted these with several different designs, pink dogwood, mixed fruit, and a yellow and blue leaf design, to name a few. Some of the refrigerator jar lids were painted a contrasting color matching that particular design. Though quite attractive, the hand painted designs are very easily damaged by strong cleaners, or abrasives, and do not take well to microwave or dishwasher use.

The trademarks you will find are those of the late 50's to the mid 60's.

PRICE GUIDE		
DESCRIPTION		CURRENT PRICES
MUG	- 8 oz.	— $3.50
BOWL, CEREAL	- 5"	— 4.00
BOWL, CUSTARD	- 6 oz.	— 3.00
BOWL, MIXING, Colonial	- 4 7/8"	— 4.00
BOWL, MIXING, Colonial	- 6"	— 5.00
BOWL, MIXING, Colonial	- 7 3/8"	— 6.00
BOWL, MIXING, Colonial	- 8 ½"	— 8.00
BOWL, BATTER, Colonial	- 7 ½"	— 14.00
CASSEROLE, FRENCH	- 12 oz.	— 4.00
CASSEROLE, Knob Cover	- 1 pt.	— 4.50
CASSEROLE, Knob Cover	- 1 qt.	— 5.50

PRICE GUIDE		
DESCRIPTION		CURRENT PRICES
CASSEROLE, Knob Cover	- 1½ qt.	— $6.50
CASSEROLE, Knob Cover	- 2 qt.	— 8.00
CASSEROLE, OVAL, Au Gratin Lid	- 1½ qt.	— 7.50
CAKE PAN, Round	- 8"	— 7.00
CAKE PAN, Square	- 8"	— 7.00
PAN, DEEP LOAF	- 5"x9"	— 6.00
DISH, OVAL, DIVIDED	- 11¾"	— 7.50
REFRIGERATOR JAR	- 4 1/8"x4 1/8"	— 7.00
REFRIGERATOR JAR	- 4 ¼"x8 ¼"	— 12.00
UTILITY PAN	- 6½"x10½"	— 8.00
UTILITY PAN	- 8"x12½"	— 9.00

Top Row: 8" Round Pan, 1½ qt. Casserole & Table Server, 1½ qt. Casserole. **Row 2:** 9" Pie Pan, 2-8" Pie Pans. **Row 3:** 1 pt. Casserole, 6 oz. Custard, 5 oz. Dessert, 6 oz. Tall Custard.

"IVORY OVENWARE"
(1948-1950's)
W400

The "Ivory Ovenware" set was made in the same style as the "Sapphire Blue" but without the "Philbe" design embossing. The lids and the table server have a part of the original embossing. This pattern, as well as all of the other "FIRE-KING" glassware, was guaranteed against oven breakage for two years.

The trademarks found on this pattern are (OVEN FIRE-KING GLASS) and (OVEN FIRE-KING WARE). The labels found on this pattern read, (NEW Ivory Fire-King THE WORLDS FINEST OVEN-GLASS guaranteed two years against oven breakage ANCHOR HOCKING GLASS CORPORATION LANCASTER OHIO U.S.A.).

The hard to find pieces are, 2 qt. and 1 qt. casseroles and their lids, table server, individual deep pie dish, and the 5 oz. dessert. These were open stock items. The rest of this pattern was sold as a set called, the "Sweetheart" baking set.

PRICE GUIDE

DESCRIPTION		CURRENT PRICES
CASSEROLE, Knob Cover	- 1 pt.	— $8.00
CASSEROLE, Knob Cover	- 1 qt.	— 10.00
CASSEROLE, Knob Cover	- 1 ½ qt.	— 12.00
CASSEROLE, Knob Cover	- 2 qt.	— 15.00
CUSTARD, Tall	- 6 oz.	— 3.00
DESSERT	- 5 oz.	— 3.00
BAKER, INDIVIDUAL	- 6 oz.	— 3.00
BAKER, DEEP PIE DISH	- 5 3/8"	— 8.00
CAKE PAN, Round	- 9"	— 6.00
PAN, DEEP LOAF	- 9 1/8"	— 6.00
PAN, PIE	- 9"	— 5.00
PAN, BAKING	- 10 ½"	— 10.00
TABLE SERVER	- 8 ½" (Bottom)	— 12.00
CUSTARD, Scalloped Edge	- 6 oz.	— 3.00
PAN, PIE	- 8"	— 5.00

Fire·King
OVEN GLASS

Heat Resisting

Easy to Clean

Guaranteed 2 Years

Made by America's Leading Glassmaker
ANCHOR-HOCKING GLASS CORP.
LANCASTER, OHIO, U. S. A.

Top Row: (Binkys Nip) Nipple Cover, 4 oz. Nurser, 8 oz. Nurser, 5 3/8" Pie Dish, 4 3/8" Pie Plate. **Row 2:** Silex 2 Cup Drip Coffeemaker, Dripolator, 9" Pie Plate, Pop-corn Popper. **Row 3:** 8 3/8" Pie Plate, 9" Pie Plate, 9 5/8" Pie Plate, Juice Saver, Pie Plate.

Top Row: 2 qt. Casserole & Table Server, 2 qt. Casserole, 1½ qt. Casserole, 1 qt. Casserole, 10 oz. Casserole. **Row 2:** Large Roaster, Small Roaster, 1½ qt. Pie Plate Cover & Casserole, 1 qt. Pie Plate, Lid & Casserole. **Row 3:** 10⅛" Mixing Bowl, 8⅜" Mixing Bowl, 6⅞" Mixing Bowl, 3 Spout Measuring Bowl. **Row 4:** Spout 1 Cup Measure, Mug, 6 oz. Custard, Tall Plain Custard, Short Plain Custard, 5 oz. Custard, 5 oz. Custard W/Rack. **Row 5:** 8½x12½ Utility Pan, Deep Loaf Pan, Large Refrigerator, Small Refrigerator.

"SAPPHIRE BLUE OVENWARE"
(1942-1948)
B3400

"Sapphire Blue" ovenware is identified by it's clear blue color with the "Philbe" design embossing on the sides, in the bottoms of each piece, and also on the covers. There are probably more people collecting this pattern of "FIRE-KING" than all other "FIRE-KING" patterns put together. There are also a few pieces in jade-ite with the "Philbe" embossing, the mug, the juice saver pie plate, and the refrigerator jars.

The hard to find pieces are, the skillet, the nipple cover, the dry measure, the juicer saver pie plate, the thin mug, the 4 3/8" bowl, and the 5 3/8" bowl. The first three are very hard to find. The rest can be found but you'll have to pay a pretty penny to get them.

The trademarks found on this pattern are, (FIRE-KING), (FIRE-KING OVEN GLASS), (FIRE-KING GUARANTEED 1 year OVEN-PROOF). The nursers and some pieces do not have trademarks.

The 1 pt square baker is the small refrigerator jar without the lid. Round bakers are the casseroles without the covers. There are three types of covers for the casseroles, the knob cover, the pie plate with two tab handles, and the single tab cover for the 10 oz. individual casserole. There are two styles of mugs, the thin (coffee) and the thick (shaving). The nursers came in two sizes 4 oz. and 8 oz. There was a nipple cover embossed "Binkys Nip" that was used with the nursers.

The juice saver pie plate differs from all the other pie plates by it's second or step back rim. By the way! The roasters do not have a top and a bottom, they are one and the same. There are two 3¼" custards, one short and one tall that do not have the "Philbe" design, they are called jam jars. There are two bowls commonly called the dessert and the cereal, Anchor Hocking lists them as, 4 3/8" pie plate and 5 3/8" individual deep pie dish. There is no listing in any of the company catalogs nor in the company archives for a dry measure, that we have found.

Like so much of the "FIRE-KING" glassware this line was used as a premium by many companies. One such company was the Octogon Soap Co. You would save the coupons on a bar of soap or box of powders until you had enough to get the piece you just had to have.

PRICE GUIDE

DESCRIPTION		CURRENT PRICES
BAKER, ROUND	- 1 pt. 5 5/8"	— $4.00
BAKER, SQUARE (Ref. no lid)	- 1 pt. 4½"x5"	— 5.00
BAKER,	- 1 qt. 7¼"	— 6.00
BAKER,	- 1½ qt. 8¼"	— 9.00
BAKER,	- 2 qt. 8 7/8"	— 10.00
CASSEROLE, IND., Tab Lid	- 10 oz. 4 ¾"	— 12.00
CASSEROLE, Knob Cover	- 1 pt. 5 5/8"	— 10.00
CASSEROLE, Knob Cover	- 1 qt. 7¼"	— 10.00
CASSEROLE, Knob Cover	- 1½ qt. 8¼"	— 12.00
CASSEROLE, Knob Cover	- 2 qt. 8 7/8"	— 15.00
CASSEROLE, Pie Plate Lid	- 1 qt., 6¾"	— 12.50
CASSEROLE, Pie Plate Lid	- 1½ qt. 8¼"	— 15.00
CASSEROLE, Pie Plate Lid	- 2 qt. 8 7/8"	— 18.00
CUSTARD, CUP	- 5 oz. 3¾"	— 3.00
CUSTARD, CUP	- 6 oz. 4"	— 3.50
CUSTARD, CUP	- 6 oz. 3 3/8"	— 3.50
CUSTARD, CUP, PLAIN, SHORT	- 6 oz. 3¼"x2¼"h	— 3.00
CUSTARD, CUP, PLAIN, TALL	- 6 oz. 3¼"x2¾"h	— 3.50
CUSTARD, CUP, BAKING RACK	- 6 cup (wire)	— 3.00
MEASURING CUP, DRY (No Spout)	- 8 oz.	— 100.00
MEASURING CUP, 1 Spout	- 8 oz.	— 15.00
MEASURING CUP, 3 Spout	- 8 oz.	— 16.00
MEASURING BOWL, 3 Spout	- 16 oz. 5 3/8"	— 18.00
MUG, HEAVY, (Shaving)*	- 8 oz.	— 19.50
MUG, THIN, (Coffee)	- 8 oz.	— 19.50
NURSER	- 4 oz.	— 14.00

PRICE GUIDE

DESCRIPTION		CURRENT PRICES
NURSER	- 8 oz.	— $18.00
PIE PLATE	- 8 3/8"	— 7.00
PIE PLATE	- 9"	— 9.00
PIE PLATE	- 9 5/8"	— 9.50
PIE PLATE, Juice Saver*	- 10 3/8"	— 70.00
PIE PLATE, BOWL	- 4 3/8"	— 10.00
PIE DISH, DEEP IND.	- 5 3/8"	— 11.00
PERCULATOR, TOP	- 2 1/8"	— 3.50
REFRIGERATOR JAR, LID*	- 4½"x5"	— 8.50
REFRIGERATOR JAR, LID*	- 5 1/8"x9 1/8"	— 27.00
ROASTER, 2 pc.	- 8¾"	— 35.00
ROASTER, 2 pc.	- 10 3/8"	— 60.00
TABLE SERVER, Tab Handles	- 8½" (Bottom)	— 12.50
UTILITY BOWL, MIXING	- 6 7/8"	— 9.00
UTILITY BOWL, MIXING	- 8 3/8"	— 12.00
UTILITY BOWL, MIXING	- 10 1/8"	— 17.00
PAN, UTILITY	- 8 1/8"x12½"	— 17.50
PAN, UTILITY	- 6 5/8"x10½"	— 15.00
PAN, DEEP LOAF	- 5 1/8x9 1/8"	— 20.00
NIPPLE COVER, (Binkys Nip)		— 100.00
SKILLET		??
NIPPLE, (Binkys Nip)		— 10.00
SILEX, DRIP, Coffee	- 2 Cup	— 20.00
W/Dripalator		— 30.00
POPCORN POPPER		— 35.00

*Add $2.00 to $5.00 for jade-ite items due to rarity.

Jade-ite Mug "Philbe" Design

Sapphire Blue Ovenware

FIRE-KING OVEN GLASS

Housewives prefer to cook in glass for they are then able to actually see their foods cooking, eliminating the possibility of improperly cooked foods. Glass is also more easily cleaned than metal utensils, saving time and labor.

A three-fold purpose—bake, serve, and store in the same dish. Fire-King oven glass is not only suitable for oven cooking but makes ideal serving dishes for the table and in addition is safe and practical for refrigerator use.

Not only does Fire-King possess unusual cooking qualities but it is attractive, a complement to any table, and above all—the lowest priced oven glass on the market.

B3405 1 Pt.
B3406 1 Qt.
B3407 1½ Qt.
B3408 2 Qt.

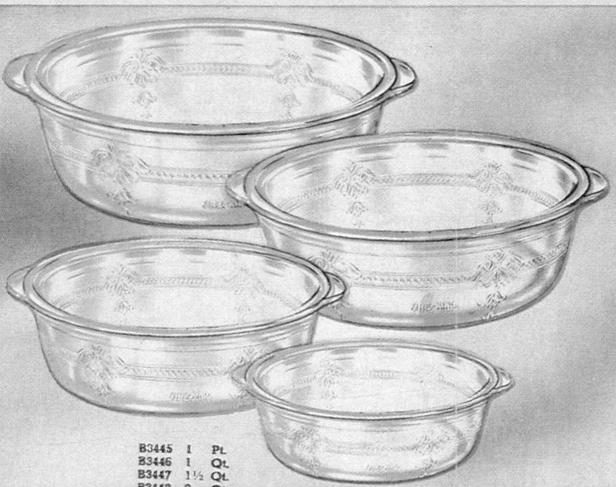

B3445 1 Pt.
B3446 1 Qt.
B3447 1½ Qt.
B3448 2 Qt.

B3466 6⅞ In.
B3467 8⅜ In.
B3469 10⅛ In.

B3497 1½ Qt.
B3498 2 Qt.

B3494 4½ In. x 5 In.
B3499 5¼ In. x 9⅛ In.

B3420 5 Oz.

Item No.	Size	Doz. to Ctn.	Wt. Ctn.	Retail Price
CASSEROLES WITH KNOB COVERS				
B3405	1 Pint	2	28 lbs.	25c Ea.
B3406	1 Quart	2	51 lbs.	35c Ea.
B3407	1½ Quart	2	63 lbs.	50c Ea.
B3408	2 Quart	1	40 lbs.	60c Ea.
CASSEROLES WITH PIE PLATE COVERS				
B3497	1½ Quart	2	66 lbs.	50c Ea.
B3498	2 Quart	1	37 lbs.	60c Ea.
INDIVIDUAL CASSEROLE & COVER				
B3402	10 Ounce	4	38 lbs.	10c Ea.
OPEN BAKERS				
B3444	1 Pint (Sq.)	4	40 lbs.	15c Ea.
B3445	1 Pint	2	16 lbs.	15c Ea.
B3446	1 Quart	2	29 lbs.	25c Ea.
B3447	1½ Quart	2	35 lbs.	35c Ea.
B3448	2 Quart	1	22 lbs.	40c Ea.
DEEP LOAF PAN				
B3409	9⅛"	2	43 lbs.	35c Ea.
UTILITY PAN				
B3410	10½"	2	45 lbs.	40c Ea.
PIE PLATES				
B3459	8⅜"	4	45 lbs.	10c Ea.
B3460	9"	3	41 lbs.	15c Ea.
B3461	9⅝"	2	35 lbs.	20c Ea.

Item No.	Size	Doz. to Ctn.	Wt. Ctn.	Retail Price
UTILITY BOWLS				
B3466	6⅞"	3	33 lbs.	10c Ea.
B3467	8⅜"	1½	28 lbs.	15c Ea.
B3469	10⅛"	1	25 lbs.	25c Ea.
TRIPLE DUTY JARS AND COVERS				
B3494	4½" x 5"	4	60 lbs.	25c Ea.
B3499	5⅛" x 9⅛"	2	70 lbs.	50c Ea.
INDIVIDUAL DEEP PIE DISH				
B3465	5⅜" x 1⅞"	3	18 lbs.	10c Ea.
INDIVIDUAL BAKERS				
B3413	6 Ounce	6	20 lbs.	5c Ea.
B3420	5 Ounce	6	17 lbs.	5c Ea.
B3421	6 Ounce	6	17 lbs.	5c Ea.

MISCELLANEOUS

Item No.		Doz. to Ctn.	Wt. Ctn.	Retail Price
B3468	8 oz. Nursing Bottle	6	34 lbs.	10c Ea.
B3464	4 oz. Nursing Bottle	6	19 lbs.	10c Ea.
B97	8 oz. Measuring Cup	4	27 lbs.	10c Ea.
B5	2⅛" Percolator Top	6	13 lbs.	5c Ea.
B885	16 oz. Measuring-Mixing Bowl	2	17 lbs.	10c Ea.

B3421 6 Oz.

B3459 8⅜ In.
B3460 9 In.
B3461 9⅝ In.

B3410 10½ In.

B3402 10 Oz.

B5 2⅛ In.

B3465 5⅜ In. x 1⅞ In.

B3409 9⅛ In.

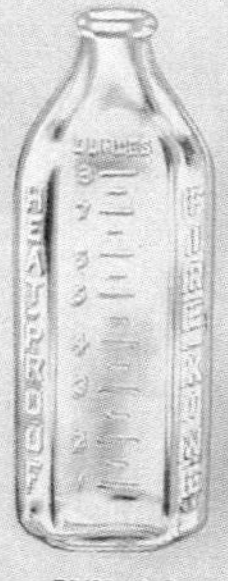

B3468 8 Oz.

B3464 4 Oz.

B97 8 Oz.

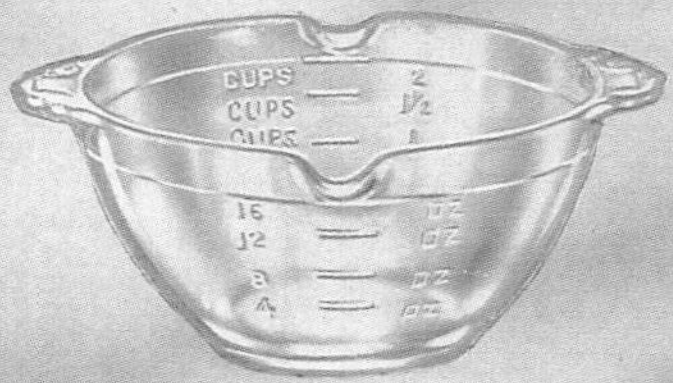

B885 16 Oz.

B3413 6 Oz.

Top Row: Sapphire Blue Refrigerator Jars. **Row 2:** Thin Oval & Round Jade-ite W/Crystal Top, Hand Painted Oval & Round. **Row 3:** Ivory Set, and Anchorwhite Set. **Row 4:** Handpainted Anchorwhite Fruit Set, Handpainted Anchorwhite Leaves Set. **Row 5:** Philbe Embossed Heavy Jade-ite Set, Plain Heavy Jade-ite With Crystal Lid, Thin Anchorwhite w/22K Gold Leaf Design.

Top Row: Ivory, Jade-ite, White. **Row 2:** Crystal, Ivory Embossed, Crystal, Pebbled Finish Crystal.

"REFRIGERATOR JARS" AND "BUTTER DISHES"

The oldest sets are the "Sapphire Blue" and the "Jade-ite" with the "Philbe" design embossing. These date back to the early 1940's, and are considerably larger and heavier than the rest. The 1950's refrigerator jars were thinner, smaller, and did not have the "Philbe" embossing. They also had clear lids which were embossed "FIRE-KING" oven ware. These jars came in several Anchor Hocking colors, jade-ite, ivory, crystal and white.

You will find some white sets with hand painted designs but, this was not done by Anchor Hocking. They sold a very large quantity of the Anchorwhite glassware to a company that did the hand painting. There is also a set of white hand painted small round, and large oval jars with clear lids which have a flower design embossing.

The butter dishes were made in the early 50's in the colors of, jade-ite, ivory, crystal, and white. All of which came with clear lids. I guess we all have our dreams. So if your looking for a turquoise blue butter dish we wish you luck. Who knows, stranger things have happened.

PRICE GUIDE

DESCRIPTION		CURRENT PRICES
JADE-ITE, SMALL THIN/Clear Lid	- 4"x4"	— $7.00
JADE-ITE, LARGE THIN/Clear Lid	- 4"x8"	— 15.00
JADE-ITE, SMALL/Jade-Ite Lid	- 4½"x5"	— 10.00
JADE-ITE, LARGE/Jade-Ite Lid	- 51/8"x91/8"	— 25.00
SAPPHIRE BLUE, SMALL/Lid	- 4½"x5"	— 10.00
SAPPHIRE BLUE, LARGE/Lid	- 51/8"x91/8"	— 30.00
IVORY, SMALL, Clear Lid	- 4"x4"	— 7.00
IVORY, LARGE, Clear Lid	- 4"x8"	— 15.00
WHITE, SMALL, Clear Lid	- 4"x4"	— 5.00
WHITE, LARGE, Clear Lid	- 4"x8"	— 10.00
WHITE, SMALL, Hand Paint, C/Lid	- 4"x4"	— 7.00
WHITE, LARGE, Hand Paint, C/Lid	- 4"x8"	— 12.00

PRICE GUIDE

DESCRIPTION		CURRENT PRICES
WHITE, SMALL, Gold Oval, C/Lid	- 4"x4"	— $7.00
WHITE, LARGE, Gold Oval, C/Lid	- 4"x8"	— 12.00
WHITE, SMALL, Rnd., Hand Painted	- 4 ¼"	— 7.00
WHITE, LARGE, Oval, Hand Painted	- 4 ¼"x9"	— 12.00
LIDS/Clear		— 1.00 — 3.00
LIDS/Colors		4.00
BUTTER DISH, Clear, Clear Lid	- 2¾"x 6¾"	— 4.00
BUTTER DISH, White, Clear Lid	- 2¾"x 6¾"	— 5.00
BUTTER DISH, Ivory, Clear Lid	- 2¾"x 6¾"	— 8.00
BUTTER DISH, Jade-Ite, Clear Lid	- 2¾"x 6¾"	— 15.00
BUTTER DISH, Ivy, Clear, Clear Lid	- 2¾" x 6¾"	— 5.00
BUTTER DISH, Turquoise, Clear Lid	- 2¾"x6¾"	??

W256   W257

BAKE, SERVE AND STORE JARS

W221

			PACKING
W256—4" x 4"	All-Purpose Jar with Crystal Fire-King Cover		2 doz. — 20 lbs.
W257—4" x 8"	All-Purpose Jar with Crystal Fire-King Cover		1 doz. — 25 lbs.
W221—7 ¼" x 2 ¾"	Quarter Pound Butter & Cover		2 doz.—17 ½ lbs.

SETS

W200/85—6 Pce. Jar Set (Each Set in Gift Ctn.) .... 6 sets — 22 lbs.
COMPOSITION: Two W256 Jars & Covers
            One W257 Jar & Cover

W200/88—12 Pce. Jar Set (Each Set in Gift Ctn.) .... 4 sets — 30 lbs.
COMPOSITION: Four W256 Jars & Covers
            Two W257 Jars & Covers

PROMOTE SETS FOR GREATER VOLUME AND FASTER SALES.

KITCHEN GLASSWARE

256	257	W256	W257

PACKING

256—4 x 4" Refrigerator Jar & Cover .... 2 doz. — 20 lbs.
257—4 x 8" Refrigerator Jar & Cover .... 1 doz. — 25 lbs.
W256—4 x 4" Refrigerator Jar & Cover .... 2 doz. — 18 lbs.
W257—4 x 8" Refrigerator Jar & Cover .... 1 doz. — 22 lbs.
W200/85—6 Pce. Refrigerator Set (Each Set in Gift Carton) .... 6 sets — 22 lbs.
Consists of Two W256 and One W257 Jars & Covers

(The above Anchorwhite Jars have Crystal Fire-King Covers)

221	W221	691	602

221—7¼ x 2¾" Quarter Pound Butter & Cover .... 2 doz. — 18 lbs.
W221—7¼ x 2¾" Quarter Pound Butter & Cover .... 2 doz. — 18 lbs.
691—1 Qt. Water Bottle W/Snow Flake Metal Cap .... 2 doz. — 41 lbs.
602—2 Qt. Water Bottle W/Snow Flake Metal Cap .... 1 doz. — 28 lbs.

See Crystal Kitchen Bowls on Page 52.

282	171	713	97

282—40 oz. Refrigerator Chiller W/Red Plastic Cap .... 1 doz. — 15 lbs.
171— 6¼ oz. Cruet & Stopper .... 2 doz. — 14 lbs.
713— 7" Juice Extractor .... 2 doz. — 35 lbs.
97— 8 oz. Measuring Cup .... 3 doz. — 25 lbs.

Percolator Tops are shown on Pages 44 and 49.

50.

Fire·King

TRIPLE PURPOSE REFRIGERATOR JARS

TWO SIZES

B3400/22—6 Pc. Bake-Serve-Store Set. Each Set consists of: Two 4½" x 5" Jars and Covers. One 5½ x 9¼" Jar and Cover.
Retail Price . . . . $1.00 Set
(For individual items, see inside spread)

Each Set packed in Chip Carton, 6 chips to a re-shipping carton, weight 36 lbs.

Bake! Serve! Store!

They Stack!

INSTRUCTIONS

A few simple rules to get the best service and longest life from Fire-King: When removing dishes from oven, be sure to place on a dry pad or dish mat. Avoid placing the glass directly on a metal table, top of oven or sink. The hot dish should not be handled with a wet cloth nor should cold water be poured into it until the dish is cool.

Do not place "Fire-King" Oven Glass directly over a flame. "Fire-King" is for use in the oven only.

PRINTED IN U.S.A.

"MIXING BOWLS"
(1940-68)

During this period Anchor Hocking made six different styles of mixing bowls. The oldest is the 1940, three piece set of the "Sapphire Blue Ovenware" utility bowls with the "Philbe" design embossing, and a rolled edge. The trademark on these bowls is ("FIRE-KING") which is embossed on the bottom and is read from the inside. The rolled edge of these bowls were called the "chip-proof edge", and was used on several mixing bowl patterns of depression era glass.

The next set was introduced in the mid 1940's and given the name "Swirl" by it's collectors. Anchor Hocking only refers to it by the individual colors. The "Swirl" mixing bowls consisted of a four piece set, and were made in five different colors, jade-ite, ivory, white, and lustre, and rainbow. Jade-ite was introduced around 1945, ivory and white 1950, lustre in 1951, and Rainbow in 1966. The Rainbow colors are fired-on sandlewood, turquoise, yellow and coral. Due to the "Swirl" patterns long production run, you will find almost every trademark Anchor Hocking used on these bowls.

About 1950 the "Beaded Rim" bowls went into production in the "FIRE-KING" colors of jade-ite, ivory, white, lustre, and later in forest green. This was a three piece set with a smooth rounded shape, and a beaded rim for strengthening and to help reduce chipping. These bowls have the trademarks of the 50's and 60's with the exception of the forest green, introduced in 1953, and never trademarked. In addition to the above colors there was an assorted fired on color set of red, yellow, blue, and green.

1950 also saw the introduction of the "Splash Proof" mixing bowls in ivory and white with several colorful painted designs. These came with the "Range Sets" so popular at the time. The color of jade-ite first came in a three piece set but later a large 4 qt. bowl was added. In 1956 a new color was added, turquoise blue in a four bowl set. The trademarks on these bowls are those of the 1950's.

As for the hard to find bowls of the "Splash Proof" design, the 4 qt. turquoise blue seems to be the most elusive. In the "Range Set" pattern, mixing bowls, the "Modern Tulip", and the "Kitchen Aids" bowls are harder to find.

In 1956 the "Swedish Modern" (or "Teardrop" as collectors like to call them) mixing bowl set was introduced in the colors of jade-ite, white, and turquoise blue. This was a four bowl set with an unique teardrop shape, thus the nickname.

The hard to find bowls are to be the 1 qt. and 2 qt. in jade-ite. In white, the only bowl we have found is the 1 pt. As for now, we have not found any catalog listings or magazine ads of this color in the "Swedish Modern" style.

PRICE GUIDE

DESCRIPTION   CURRENT PRICES

"SAPPHIRE BLUE OVENWARE"
(1940-1948)

MIXING BOWL	- 10 1/8"	— $16.00
MIXING BOWL	- 8 3/8"	— 12.00
MIXING BOWL	- 6 7/8"	— 10.00

"SWIRL" (1949-1972)
(Jade-Ite, Ivory, Lustre, White And Rainbow)

MIXING BOWL	- 9"	— $12.00
MIXING BOWL	- 8"	— 10.00
MIXING BOWL	- 7"	— 8.00
MIXING BOWL	- 6"	— 6.00

"BEADED RIM" (1950-1964)
(Jade-Ite, Ivory, Lustre, White, Forest Green And Colored)

MIXING BOWL	- 8 3/8"	— $8.00
MIXING BOWL	- 7 1/4"	— 7.00
MIXING BOWL	- 6"	— 6.00
MIXING BOWL	- 4 7/8"	— 5.00

PRICE GUIDE

DESCRIPTION   CURRENT PRICES

"SPLASH PROOF" (1957-1960)
(Jade-Ite, Ivory, White, Turquoise Blue)

MIXING BOWL	- 9½" 4 qt.	— $15.00
MIXING BOWL	- 8½" 3 qt.	— 12.00
MIXING BOWL	- 7 5/8" 2 qt.	— 10.00
MIXING BOWL	- 6 ¾" 1 qt.	— 8.00

"SWEDISH MODERN" (TEARDROP) (1954-1958)
(Jade-Ite, Turquoise Blue And White)

MIXING BOWL	- 8 ¾" 3 qt.	— $16.00
MIXING BOWL	- 6 ¾" 2 qt.	— 14.00
MIXING BOWL	- 6 ¼" 1 qt.	— 12.00
MIXING BOWL	- 5 ¼" 1 pt.	— 10.00

"COLONIAL RIM" (1960-1971)
(Jade-Ite, Ivory, Lustre, White And White/Colored Band)

MIXING BOWL	- 8 ½"	— $10.00
MIXING BOWL	- 7 3/8"	— 8.00
MIXING BOWL	- 6"	— 6.00
MIXING BOWL	- 4 7/8"	— 5.00

(Add 2.00 Per Bowl For Colors And Floral Designs)
NOTE: As a rule you can add 2 to 3 dollars to the price of the jade-ite, turquoise blue and hand painted bowls due to their popularity.

Fire·King

4 PURPOSE UTILITY BOWLS

- Mix!
- Bake!
- Serve!
- Store!

Low in Price

GUARANTEE

Any Fire-King dish or cover which breaks from oven heat within two years after date of purchase, will be replaced without charge by any store handling Fire-King Oven Glass in exchange for the broken pieces. This guarantee does not apply in the case of breakage due to any cause other than "from oven heat." All stores making replacements as above outlined will deduct in their next remittance to us for the value of these replacements. Such deductions will be promptly allowed.

THE MODERN SCIENTIFIC BAKING WARE

B3400/34—3 PC. SET
Each Set in Individual Chip Carton, six Individuals to an Outer. Wt. 30 lbs.
Retail Price......50c Set

Top Row: Anchorwhite & Sunbeam Bowl. **Row 2:** Jade-ite. **Row 3:** Ivory. **Row 4:** Lustre.

Top Row: Lustre. **Row 2:** Ivory. **Row 3:** Anchorwhite. **Row 4:** Jade-ite.

Top Row: Colonial Jade-ite. **Row 2:** Colonial Anchorwhite. **Row 3:** Fire-King Sapphire Blue. **Row 4:** W-400 Line of Anchorwhite.

Top Row: Splash Proof Jade-ite, Anchorwhite. **Row 2:** Swedish Modern (Teardrop), Jade-ite, Anchorwhite. **Row 3:** Splash Proof Jade-ite, Ivory. **Row 4:** Turquoise Blue Swedish Modern (Teardrop).

JADE-ITE *Fire-King* ® GLASSWARE

G384 — G327

★ G291

★ G1212

G39

PACKING

G384—9 oz.	St. Denis Cup		4 doz. —	24 lbs.
G327—5 ⅞"	Saucer		4 doz. —	19 lbs.
★ G291—5"	Soup or Cereal		4 doz. —	33 lbs.
★ G1212—8 oz.	Coffee Mug		4 doz. —	32 lbs.
G39—	Egg Cup		6 doz. —	44 lbs.

Fire-King

"SPLASH-PROOF" BOWLS

G255

G367 — G368 — G369 — G300/166

G255—20 oz. Milk Pitcher			3 doz. —	36 lbs.
G367— 2 Qt. Mixing Bowl			1 doz. —	23 lbs.
G368— 3 Qt. Mixing Bowl			1 doz. —	29 lbs.
G369— 4 Qt. Mixing Bowl			1 doz. —	38 lbs.
G300/166— 3 Pce. Mixing Bowl Set			1 doz. —	90 lbs.
(BULK Pkd. in 3 Ctns.)			sets	

COMP.: One each G367, G368 and G369 Bowl

See Other Jade-ite Mixing Bowls
on Page 36.

ANCHORWHITE MIXING BOWLS

PACKING

W4100/5 —4 Pce. Mixing Bowl Set   6 sets — 41 lbs.
(Each Set in Gift Carton)
W4100/55—4 Pce. Mixing Bowl Set   2 dz. sets —152 lbs.
(Bulk Packed in 6 Cartons)
W4100/67—4 Pce. Mixing Bowl Set   8 sets — 48 lbs.
(Each Set Nested in a Cell)

The Sets listed above consist of one each of the 6″, 7″, 8″ and 9″ Bowls.

W4100/107—4 Pce. Mixing Bowl Set   2 dz. sets —109 lbs.
(Bulk Packed in 5 Cartons)
W4100/109—4 Pce. Mixing Bowl Set   8 sets — 33 lbs.
(Each Set Nested in a Cell)

The two Sets listed above consist of one each of the 5″, 6″, 7″ and 8″ Bowls.

OPEN STOCK

W4155—5″ Mixing Bowl .... 2 doz. — 15 lbs.
W4156—6″ Mixing Bowl .... 2 doz. — 19 lbs.
W4157—7″ Mixing Bowl .... 2 doz. — 31 lbs.
W4158—8″ Mixing Bowl .... 1 doz. — 22 lbs.
W4159—9″ Mixing Bowl .... 1 doz. — 29 lbs.

BATTER BOWL

W655—3½ Pt. Handled Batter Bowl .... 1 doz. — 22 lbs.

See Page 48 for this same Batter Bowl in Jade-ite and Page 50 for a White Bowl with a Red Band.

PACKING

W300/130—3 Pce. Mixing Bowl Set   2 dz. sets — 66 lbs.
(Bulk Packed in 3 Cartons)
COMPOSITION: One each 4⅞″, 6″ and 7¼″ Bowls

OPEN STOCK

W355—4⅞″ Mixing Bowl .... 2 doz. — 13 lbs.
W356—6″   Mixing Bowl .... 2 doz. — 20 lbs.
W357—7¼″ Mixing Bowl .... 2 doz. — 33 lbs.
W358—8⅜″ Mixing Bowl .... 1 doz. — 27 lbs.

"COLONIAL KITCHEN" DESIGN

W800/141—3 Pce. Mixing Bowl Set .... 8 sets — 35 lbs.
(Each Set Nested in a Cell)
COMPOSITION: One each 6″, 7³⁄₁₆″ and 8¾″ Bowls

OPEN STOCK

W856—6″   Mixing Bowl .... 2 doz. — 20 lbs.
W857—7³⁄₁₆″ Mixing Bowl .... 2 doz. — 32 lbs.
W859—8¾″ Mixing Bowl .... 1 doz. — 27 lbs.

HEAT-PROOF

Top Row: Handpainted Band Anchorwhite, Graduated Crystal, Handpainted 1″ Band. **Row 2:** Ivory, Crystal, Anchorwhite. **Row 3:** Forest Green, Jade-ite ½″ Band, Jade-ite 1″ Band, Lustre ½″ Band.

Top Row: Fired-On Green 5 3/8″, Jade-ite 5 3/8″ w/lid, Jade-ite 7½″ Kitchen, Ivory 7½″ Kitchen. **Row 2:** Crystal 5 3/8″ w/lid, Forest Green 5 3/8″ w/lid, Forest Green 6″ w/lid, Forest Green 7½″ w/lid.

"FIRE-KING" BATTER BOWLS
(1950-70)

The "Batter Bowl" is a 2 ½ qt. mixing bowl with a pouring spout on one end and a large handle on the other. There are three different styles, the 3/4" band, the 1" band and tab handle, and were made in the colors of jade-ite, ivory, crystal, lustre, turquoise blue, white and white with hand painted fruit and flower designs. The oldest style is the 3/4" band that carries the 1950's trademarks. The 1" band was introduced in the 60's to match a set of mixing bowls with the 1" band and carries the Anchor Hocking "FIRE-KING" trademarks of the 1960's. As for the tab handle batter bowl it has a splash proof mixing bowl shape with a large tab handle on one end and a pouring spout on the other. This bowl was made in forest green and is not trademarked. The hand painted anchorwhite bowls, as with all of the hand painted patterns was not done by Anchor Hocking. This will be covered in more detail later.

The rarest "Batter Bowl" is the turquoise blue which is in very short supply and is the pride of any "Turquoise Blue" collector. We have not found any company catalog listings or magazine ads on this bowl yet. Due to the very short run of this color and it's apparent popularity this bowl has sky rocketed in price over the last year.

There are two crystal batter bowls that have graduations like those of a measuring cup. These bowls were made in the mid 60's.

PRICE GUIDE

DESCRIPTION				CURRENT PRICES	
1" BAND	- 7½"	(Hand Painted)	$14.00	Row 1:	#1
MEAUSIRNG	- 2 qt.	(Crystal)	10.00		#2
MEASURING	- 1 qt.	(Crystal)	8.00	Not Shown	
1" BAND	- 7½"	(Hand Painted)	14.00		#3
1" BAND	- 7½"	(White)	10.00	Row 2:	#1
3/4" BAND	- 7½"	(Crystal)	8.00		#2
3/4" BAND	- 7½"	(Ivory)	14.00	Not Shown	
1" BAND	- 7½"	(Ivory)	12.00		#3
TAB HANDLE	- 7½"	(Forest Green)	15.00	Row 3:	#1
3/4" BAND	- 7½"	(Jade-Ite)	15.00		#2
1" BAND	- 7½"	(Jade-Ite)	12.00		#3
1" BAND	- 7½"	(Lustre)	15.00		#4
3/4" BAND	- 7½"	(Turquoise Blue)	55.00	Not Shown	

"RIBBED BOWLS"
(1940's-1950's)
700

These bowls were produced as both a four piece kitchen bowl set and by adding lids to the three smallest bowls, a canister set. They were produced in several Anchor Hocking colors, jade-ite, ivory, forest green, crystal and several fired on colors on crystal. The ribbed design has been compared to the ribbed design on the "Jane Ray" tableware, this accounts for many collectors calling them "Jane Ray" bowls.

The lids are crystal, slightly domed, with raised rings in the center, then ribs that run from just off center to just over the edge of the dome. There are four bowls in the kitchen bowl set, and three bowls with lids in the canister set. The 5 3/8" bowl was offered in a four piece set of covered bowls in pastel fired-on colors of pink, ivory, green and blue with crystal lids. These bowls actually got their start in the 30's as vitrock. What we will cover here are the "FIRE-KING" colors.

These bowl are not trademarked and we have not found any pieces with the labels still intact.

The hard to find pieces are the 4¾" and 9" kitchen bowls. The large 6" crystal lid is somewhat harder to locate than the 5 3/8" and 4¾" lids.

PRICE GUIDE

DESCRIPTION		FOREST/G.	-	JADE-ITE	-	CRYSTAL	-	FIRED/ON/COLORS	-	IVORY	CURRENT PRICES
BOWL, KITCHEN	- 4¾"	— $5.00		— $5.00		— $4.00		— N/A		— $5.00	
BOWL, KITCHEN	- 5 3/8"	— 4.00		— 6.00		— 5.00		— 4.50		— 6.00	
BOWL, KITCHEN	- 6"	— 7.00		— 7.00		— 6.00		— N/A		— 7.00	
BOWL, KITCHEN	- 7½"	— 8.00		— 8.00		— 7.00		— N/A		— 8.00	
BOWL, KITCHEN	- 9"	— 10.00		— 10.00		— 9.00		— N/A		— 10.00	
LID,	- 4¾"					— 2.50					
LID,	- 5 3/8"					— 3.50					
LID,	- 6"					— 4.50					

Mixing Bowls

photo ref.	description	item order no.	shipper doz.	lbs.	price doz.
	CRYSTAL				
A	½ qt. mixing bowl	355	2	15	
B	1 qt. mixing bowl	356	2	23	
C	1½ qt. mixing bowl	357	2	39	
D	2½ qt. mixing bowl	358	1	29	
	ANCHOR WHITE				
E	½ qt. mixing bowl	W455E	1	8	
F	1 qt. mixing bowl	W456E	1	12	
G	1½ qt. mixing bowl	W457	1	18	
H	2½ qt. mixing bowl	W458	1	26	
	BATTER BOWL				
I	1 qt. graduated handled bowl	H89	1	24	
J	2 qt. graduated handled bowl	H88	½	18	

The table header spans: BULK PACKED (BY DOZEN) over item order no., shipper (doz. / lbs.), price doz.

NOTE: *See index for additional listings of Crystal and Anchor White bulk and gift items.*

Food Preparation Bulk

FP

1975 Anchor Hocking Catalog

KITCHEN BOWLS

CRYSTAL

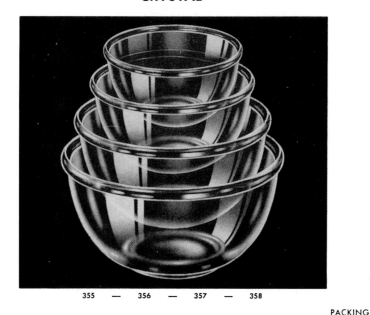

355 — 356 — 357 — 358

		PACKING
355—4 ⅞″	Mixing Bowl	3 doz. — 19 lbs.
356—6″	Mixing Bowl	3 doz. — 32 lbs.
357—7 ¼″	Mixing Bowl	3 doz. — 54 lbs.
358—8 ⅜″	Mixing Bowl	1 doz. — 28 lbs.
300/128—3 Pce. Mixing Bowl Set		3 dz. sets—105 lbs.
	Bulk Packed in 3 Cartons	
	COMPOSITION: One each 355, 356 and 357 Mixing Bowls	
300/134—4 Pce. Mixing Bowl Set		3 dz. sets—189 lbs.
	Bulk Packed in 6 Cartons	
	COMPOSITION: One each 355, 356, 357 and 358 Mixing Bowls	

See Other Mixing Bowl Sets on Pages 30, 31, 32 and 33.

Kitchen Bowls are big selling numbers — every housewife is a prospect.
Keep a variety on sale at all times.

761

365

655

761—5″	Kitchen Bowl	6 doz. — 37 lbs.
365—5 ⅝″	Splash-Proof Bowl	3 doz. — 33 lbs.
655—3 ½ Pt.	Handled Batter Bowl	1 doz. — 22 lbs.

**See Handled Batter Bowl in Jade-ite
Glass on Page 30.**

Top Row: Jade-ite. Row 2: Ivory. Row 3: Anchorwhite.

Top Row: Red Polka Dot. Row 2: Black Polka Dot. Row 3: Apples. Row 4: Tulips (Ivory or White).

"RANGE SETS"
(1950-1962)

The "Range Sets" consist of a grease jar, salt and pepper shakers, with some having a four piece set of mixing bowls. These were made with the "FIRE-KING" formula glass, and in the Anchor Hocking colors of milk white, ivory, and jade-ite. The milk white and ivory colors also had many different painted designs.

The earliest "FIRE-KING" "Range Sets" were not trademarked, and the grease jar had a screw top lid. These were made in the mid 40's through the early 50's in jade-ite, ivory, and milk white. Their shape is a slightly tapering, series of alternating, bulging, large and small rings. The metal lids are painted off white with a red ring around the edge, and three potted tulips, two yellow, and one red. If you look closely at the sides of the lids you will find (53-NKCT, ANCHOR HOCKING, U.S.A.) on the salt and pepper, and (83-CT, ANCHOR HOCKING, U.S.A.) on the grease jar lid. These range sets used the beaded rim mixing bowls.

In the early 50's Anchor Hocking introduced several new "Range Sets" in milk white, and ivory with painted designs. These came with a four piece set of mixing bowls in the sharply tapered "Splash Proof" style. The grease jar is made in the same style as the mixing bowls, (measures 5 5/8" across the top) with an early style glass knob lid. There are two different lids used on the shakers, the tulip lid described earlier, and the solid white lid with a large Devile style letter S (salt) or P (pepper). The Devile lids are marked on their sides (53 ANCHOR-NKCT; ANCHOR HOCKING, U.S.A.) in very small print. The Devile style lid was used on all of the "Splash Proof" style "Range Sets" with the exception of the "Tulip" sets, which used the tulip lids. There are eight different patterns in the "Splash Proof" style, "TULIPS" (ivory and white), "APPLES" (white with red apples and green leafs), "BLACK POLKA DOTS", "RED POLKA DOTS", "MODERN TULIP" (red and black floral pattern), "STRIPES" (Note: the "stripes" set used the Colonial mixing bowls with each having a different colored band matching one of the stripes on the grease jar, red, blue, and yellow.) And the "KITCHEN-AIDE" (white with red rolling pin, eggs, salt shaker, mixing spoon, egg beater, measuring cup, and large fork). We have found a solid white "Splash Proof" grease jar and lid but haven't found any listings in company catalogs or ads.

The (OVEN Fire-King WARE MADE IN U.S.A.) trademark is used on all the pieces with the exception of the salt and pepper shakers and the early screw top grease jars.

The hard to find items are, a good salt shaker lid of any pattern, the "STRIPED" mixing bowl set, and the "KITCHEN-AIDE" salt and pepper shakers.

Top Row: Kitchen Aids. **Row 2:** Stripes. **Row 3:** Modern Tulips.

SCREW CAP RANGE SET (1952-54)

GREASE JAR, (Jade-ite)	- 3¼"w x 4¼"h	— $10.00
SHAKER, SALT OR PEPPER	- 2"w x 4¼"h	— 6.00
MIXING BOWL, Beaded Rim	- 7¼"	— 10.00
MIXING BOWL, Beaded Rim	- 6"	— 8.00
MIXING BOWL, Beaded Rim	- 4 7/8"	— 6.00
GREASE JAR, (Ivory)	- 3¼"w x 4¼"h	— 10.00
SHAKER, SALT OR PEPPER	- 2"w x 4¼"h	— 6.00
MIXING BOWL, Beaded Rim	- 7¼"	— 8.00
MIXING BOWL, Beaded Rim	- 6"	— 6.00
MIXING BOWL, Beaded Rim	- 4 7/8"	— 5.00
GREASE JAR, (White)	- 3¼"w x 4¼"h	— 8.00
SHAKER, SALT OR PEPPER	- 2"w x 4¼"h	— 5.00
MIXING BOWL, Beaded Rim	- 7¼"	— 6.00
MIXING BOWL, Beaded Rim	- 6"	— 5.00
MIXING BOWL, Beaded Rim	- 4 7/8"	— 4.00

"TULIPS" (1953-58)
(IVORY AND WHITE)

GREASE JAR, Knob Lid	- 5 5/8" 1 pt.	— $12.00
SHAKERS, SALT OR PEPPER	- 2"w x 4¼"h	— 7.00
MIXING BOWL (Splash Proof)	- 9½" 4 qt.	— 15.00
MIXING BOWL (Splash Proof)	- 8½" 3 qt.	— 12.00
MIXING BOWL (Splash Proof)	- 7 5/8" 2 qt.	— 10.00
MIXING BOWL (Splash Proof)	- 6¾" 1 qt.	— 8.00

"APPLES" (1957)
(WHITE)

GREASE JAR, Knob Lid	- 5 5/8" 1 pt.	— $12.00
SHAKERS, SALT OR PEPPER	- 2" w x 4¼"h	— 7.00
MIXING BOWL, (Splash Proof)	- 9½" 4 qt.	— 14.00
MIXING BOWL, (Splash Proof)	- 8½" 3 qt.	— 12.00
MIXING BOWL, (Splash Proof)	- 7 5/8" 2 qt.	— 10.00
MIXING BOWL, (Splash Proof)	- 6¾" 1 qt.	— 8.00

"POLKA DOT"
(1955-56 RED) OR (1955 BLACK DOT)

GREASE JAR, Knob Lid	- 5 5/8" 1 pt.	— $12.00
SHAKERS, SALT OR PEPPER	- 2"w x 4¼"h	— 7.00
MIXING BOWL, Splash Proof	- 9½" 4 qt.	— 14.00
MIXING BOWL, Splash Proof	- 8½" 3 qt.	— 12.00
MIXING BOWL, Splash Proof	- 7 5/8" 2 qt.	— 10.00
MIXING BOWL, Splash Proof	- 6¾" 1 qt.	— 8.00

"MODERN TULIPS" (1959-60)

GREASE JAR, Knob Lid	- 5 5/8" 1 pt.	— $12.00
SHAKERS, SALT OR PEPPER	- 2"w x 4½"h	— 7.00
MIXING BOWL, Splash Proof	- 9½" 4 qt.	— 14.00
MIXING BOWL, Splash Proof	- 8½" 3 qt.	— 12.00
MIXING BOWL, Splash Proof	- 7 5/8" 2 qt.	— 10.00
MIXING BOWL, Splash Proof	- 6¾" 1 qt.	— 8.00

"STRIPES" (1960-62)

GREASE JAR, Knob Lid	- 5 5/8" 1 pt.	— $12.00
SHAKERS, SALT OR PEPPER	- 2"w x 4¼"h	— 7.00
MIXING BOWL, Colonial (Coral band)	- 8½"	— 14.00
MIXING BOWL, Colonial (Turquoise band)	- 7 3/8"	— 12.00
MIXING BOWL, Colonial (Yellow band)	- 6"	— 10.00

"KITCHEN-AIDES" (1959)

GREASE JAR, Knob Lid	- 5 5/8" 1 pt.	— $14.00
SHAKERS, SALT OR PEPPER	- 2"w x 4¼"h	— 8.00
MIXING BOWL, Splash Proof	- 9½" 4 qt.	— 14.00
MIXING BOWL, Splash Proof	- 8½" 3 qt.	— 12.00
MIXING BOWL, Splash Proof	- 7 5/8" 2 qt.	— 10.00
MIXING BOWL, Splash Proof	- 6¾" 1 qt.	— 8.00

(No lid deduct $1.00 on shakers and $2.00 on grease jar.)

OPEN STOCK

W4156—6" Mixing Bowl	2 doz.	19 lbs.
W4157—7" Mixing Bowl	2 doz.	29 lbs.
W4158—8" Mixing Bowl	1 doz.	22 lbs.
W4159—9" Mixing Bowl	1 doz.	29 lbs.

"KITCHEN AIDS" DECORATION

W300/237—3 Pce. Mixing Bowl Set
Each Set Nested & Packed in an Individual Cell,
8 Sets to Shipping Carton — 44 lbs.
COMPOSITION: One 1 Qt. Mixing Bowl
            One 2 Qt. Mixing Bowl
            One 3 Qt. Mixing Bowl

W300/238—4 Pce. Mixing Bowl Set
Each Set in Gift Carton, 4 Sets to Shipping Carton — 37 lbs.
COMPOSITION: One 1 Qt. Mixing Bowl
            One 2 Qt. Mixing Bowl
            One 3 Qt. Mixing Bowl
            One 4 Qt. Mixing Bowl

RANGE SET

W300/239—4 Pce. Range Set
   Each Set in Gift Carton, 8 Sets to Shipping Carton — 19 lbs.
COMPOSITION: One Salt Shaker—White Top
                 One Pepper Shaker—White Top
                 One Range Jar & Cover

The above Range Set and matching Mixing Bowl
Sets in "Kitchen Aids" decoration, are not
available in Open Stock.

IVORY HEAT-PROOF MIXING BOWLS

VERY CLEAN LOOKING AND PRACTICAL

W355 — 4⅞"
MIXING BOWL
Packs 3 doz.—19 #

W356 — 6"
MIXING BOWL
Packs 3 doz.—32 #

W357 — 7¼"
MIXING BOWL
Packs 3 doz.—48 #

W300/130 — 3 Pce.
MIXING BOWL SET
3 doz. sets Bulk Packed in 3 Ctns.—99 #
COMPOSITION:
One 4⅞" Mixing Bowl
One 6" Mixing Bowl
One 7¼" Mixing Bowl

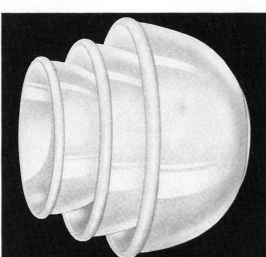

IVORY KITCHEN SETS ARE ALWAYS GOOD

W300/132—6 Pce.
KITCHEN SET
Each Set Pkd. in Gift Ctn.,
6 Sets to R/S Ctn.—32 #
COMPOSITION:
One 4⅞" Mixing Bowl
One 6" Mixing Bowl
One 7¼" Mixing Bowl
One 4¼" Salt Shaker—
Floral Top
One 4¼" Pepper Shaker—
Floral Top
One 16 oz. Canister—
Floral Top

Gift Packed

Each Set packed in Gift Carton. Makes an excellent gift. Capitalize on Sets— they raise Dollar Volume fast. Every home-maker has a place for a low-priced set like this.

JADE-ITE HEAT-PROOF MIXING BOWLS

COLORFUL AND EASILY CLEANED

G355 — 4⅞"
MIXING BOWL
Packs 3 doz.—19 #

G356 — 6"
MIXING BOWL
Packs 3 doz.—32 #

G357 — 7¼"
MIXING BOWL
Packs 3 doz.—53 #

G300/129 — 3 Pce.
MIXING BOWL SET
3 doz. sets Bulk Packed in 3 Ctns.—104 #
COMPOSITION:
One 4⅞" Mixing Bowl
One 6" Mixing Bowl
One 7¼" Mixing Bowl

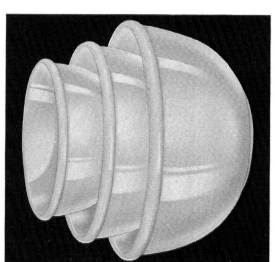

THIS IS A VERY POPULAR KITCHEN SET

G300/131—6 Pce.
KITCHEN SET
Each Set Pkd. in Gift Ctn.,
6 Sets to R/S Ctn.—32 #
COMPOSITION:
One 4⅞" Mixing Bowl
One 6" Mixing Bowl
One 7¼" Mixing Bowl
One 4¼" Salt Shaker—
Floral Top
One 4¼" Pepper Shaker—
Floral Top
One 16 oz. Canister—
Floral Top

Gift Packed

Each set packed in Gift Carton. Makes an excellent gift. Women will buy readily for themselves whatever looks good enough to give as a gift to another. Feature these sets.

DECORATED MIXING BOWL AND RANGE SETS

The deep Splash-Proof Bowl Sets are the most efficient Mixing Bowls ever produced. They are **HEAT-PROOF**— made of Fire-King ovenglass.

APPLE DECORATION

W300/219—4 Pce. Mixing Bowl Set
Each Set in Gift Carton, 4 Sets to Shipping Carton — 37 lbs.
COMPOSITION: One 1 Qt. Mixing Bowl—Apple Dec.
One 2 Qt. Mixing Bowl—Apple Dec.
One 3 Qt. Mixing Bowl—Apple Dec.
One 4 Qt. Mixing Bowl—Apple Dec.

W300/220—4 Pce. Range Set—Apple Decoration
Each Set in Gift Carton, 8 Sets to Shipping Carton — 19 lbs.
COMPOSITION: One Salt Shaker—Ivory Top
One Pepper Shaker—Ivory Top
One Range Jar & Cover

HERE IS AN IMPORTANT SELLING POINT. THE RANGE SETS MATCH THE BOWL SETS. DISPLAY THE TWO TOGETHER AND WATCH THEM MOVE OFF YOUR COUNTERS.

HEAT-PROOF

Display the Range Set with the Matching "Splash-Proof" Bowl Set for fast sales. Exposed to your trade together, they sell at once.

TULIP DECORATION

W300/148—4 Pce. Mixing Bowl Set
Each Set in Gift Carton, 4 Sets to Shipping Carton — 37 lbs.
COMPOSITION: One 1 Qt. Mixing Bowl—Tulip Dec.
One 2 Qt. Mixing Bowl—Tulip Dec.
One 3 Qt. Mixing Bowl—Tulip Dec.
One 4 Qt. Mixing Bowl—Tulip Dec.

W300/150—4 Pce. Range Set—Tulip Decoration
Each Set in Gift Carton, 8 Sets to Shipping Carton — 19 lbs.
COMPOSITION: One Salt Shaker—Tulip Top
One Pepper Shaker—Tulip Top
One Range Jar & Cover

ALL OF THE ABOVE ARE AVAILABLE ONLY IN SET PACKING.

26.

"SPLASH-PROOF" MIXING BOWLS
AND
MATCHING RANGE SETS

W300/182

W300/182—4 Pce. Mixing Bowl Set—Red

    Each Set in Gift Carton, 4 Sets to Shipping Carton, Wt. 38 lbs.
COMPOSITION:

    One 1-Qt. Mixing Bowl
    One 2-Qt. Mixing Bowl
    One 3-Qt. Mixing Bowl
    One 4-Qt. Mixing Bowl

These Mixing Bowls are the most efficient ones ever produced. Their deep sides prevent the splashing which occurs in shallow bowls. Excellent to use with portable mixers — a joy to use when mixing with spoon or hand beater.

W300/183

W300/183—4 Pce. Range Set—Red

    Each Set in Gift Carton, 8 Sets to Shipping Carton, Wt. 20 lbs.
COMPOSITION:

    One Salt Shaker—Ivory Top
    One Pepper Shaker—Ivory Top
    One Range Jar & Cover

The Sets shown on this page are NOT Available in Bulk Packing.

W300/185

W300/185—4 Pce. Range Set—Black

    Each Set in Gift Carton, 8 Sets to Shipping Carton, Wt. 20 lbs.
COMPOSITION:

    One Salt Shaker—Ivory Top
    One Pepper Shaker—Ivory Top
    One Range Jar & Cover

See Other Mixing Bowls on Pages 30 and 31.

W300/184

W300/184—4 Pce. Mixing Bowl Set—Black

    Each Set in Gift Carton, 4 Sets to Shipping Carton, Wt. 38 lbs.
COMPOSITION:

    One 1-Qt. Mixing Bowl
    One 2-Qt. Mixing Bowl
    One 3-Qt. Mixing Bowl
    One 4-Qt. Mixing Bowl

HEAT-PROOF

32.

DECORATED BOWLS AND RANGE SET

HEAT-RESISTANT

PACKING

W800/142—3 Pce. Mixing Bowl Set .... 8 sets — 35 lbs.
    (Each Set Nested in a Cell)
COMPOSITION:
    One 6"   Mixing Bowl—Yellow Band
    One 7³⁄₁₆" Mixing Bowl—Turquoise Band
    One 8¾" Mixing Bowl—Coral Band

OPEN STOCK

W856/5967—6"   Mixing Bowl—Yellow Band ...... 2 doz. — 20 lbs.
W857/5968—7³⁄₁₆" Mixing Bowl—Turq. Band .... 2 doz. — 32 lbs.
W859/5969—8¾" Mixing Bowl—Coral Band .... 1 doz. — 27 lbs.

PACKING

W300/251—4 Pce. Range Set .... 8 sets — 19 lbs.
    (Each Set in a Gift Carton)
COMPOSITION:
    One W323-S/5970 Salt Shaker—White Top
    One W323-P/5970 Pepper Shaker—White Top
    One   W365/5970 Range Jar & Cover

OPEN STOCK

W323-S/5970—4½" Salt—White Top .... 2 doz. — 9 lbs.
W323-P/5970—4½" Pepper—White Top .... 2 doz. — 9 lbs.
    (The Range Jar & Cover is not available in Open Stock)

HEAT-RESISTANT

BATTER BOWL

W655/5973—3½ Pt. Batter Bowl—Red Band .... 1 doz. — 25 lbs.

See Jade-ite and Plain Anchorwhite Batter Bowls
on Pages 43 and 45.

The Mixing Bowls in Solid Colors
are Not Available in Open Stock.

W300/149—4 Pce. Mixing Bowl Set..................... 6 sets — 30 lbs.
    (Each Set in Gift Carton)
W300/204—4 Pce. Mixing Bowl Set .... 8 sets — 42 lbs.
    (Each Set Nested in a Cell)

Each of the above Sets consists of the following:

    One 4⅞"   Mixing Bowl—Green
    One 6"   Mixing Bowl—Blue
    One 7¼" Mixing Bowl—Yellow
    One 8⅜" Mixing Bowl—Red

46.

"SNACK SETS"
(1940-1976)

The "Snack Sets" came in four place boxed sets (4 trays and 4 cups), and were very popular as shower and party gifts. The trays or plates, whichever the case, are easily identified by the cup indent which is usually found in the corner of the tray, and to one side of the plate. The cups are usually made from the punch cup molds in the 5 oz. size, with the exception of the "Hostess Delight" sets of the late 50's which used the larger 8 oz standard cups. In the late 60's the "Mosaic" snack set used the 7 ½ oz stacking cup.

The 1940 snack sets used crystal trays, and royal ruby 5 oz cups, then in the mid 50's offered sets with forest green cups. With the introduction of the turquoise blue (B4000 line) tableware came the "Hostess Delight" snack sets with 9" plates, and 8 oz cups trimmed in 22k gold in the colors of turquoise blue, ivory, and white. One of the last snack sets issued during the "FIRE-KING" years was the "Golden Shell" set in the late 60's with a 10" plate, and a 8 oz cup trimmed in 22k gold.

The only snack sets trademarked are the B4000, and W2300 lines. The B4000 line (turquoise blue, ivory, and white) sets are marked (OVEN Fire-King WARE MADE IN U.S.A.) and the W2300 line ("Golden Shell"), W4600 line ("MOSAIC") marked (Anchor Hocking OVEN Fire-King WARE MADE IN U.S.A.).

The hard to find sets are the early 40's sets, the ivory, white B4000 line and the "Sheaths of Wheat" in jade-ite. Boxed sets can be found in most all of the snack sets, and for some reason can be bought for a little less than if you bought each piece separately.

PRICE GUIDE

DESCRIPTION		CURRENT PRICES
TRAY, FAN, CRYSTAL (1940-50's)	- 10¾"x7 5/8"	— $5.00
CUP, Royal Ruby Or Forest Green	- 5 oz.	— 3.50
TRAY, RECT. Crystal Serve-A-Snak	- 11"x6"	— 4.00
CUP, Crystal Serva-Snack	- 5 oz.	— 4.00
TRAY, OVAL, CRYSTAL (1940-50's)	- 10¼"x5 1/8"	— 4.00
CUP, Royal Ruby Or Forest Green	- 5 oz.	— 3.50
PLATE, Turq. Blue, Gold Trim (1956)	- 9"	— 6.00
CUP, Turq. Blue, Gold Trim (1956)	- 8 oz.	— 3.50
PLATE, IVORY, Veil Gold Trim (1956)	- 9"	— 6.00
CUP, IVORY, Gold Trim (1956)	- 8 oz.	— 3.50
PLATE, WHITE, Gold Trim (1956)	- 9"	— 6.00*
CUP, WHITE, Gold Trim (1956)	- 8 oz.	— 3.50*
TRAY, CRY. "Sheaths Of Wheat, 1957"	- 10"x7"	— 5.00*
CUP, CRY. "Sheaths Of Wheat, 1957"	- 6½ oz.	— 3.00*
TRAY, JADE-ITE, "Sheaths Of Wheat"	- 10"x7"	— 10.00*
CUP, JADE-ITE, "Sheaths Of Wheat"(1957)	- 6½ oz.	— 5.00*
TRAY, RECT. "Fleurette" (1958)	- 11"x6"	— 3.00
CUP, RECT. "Fleurette" (1958)	- 5 oz.	— 1.50

PRICE GUIDE

DESCRIPTION		CURRENT PRICES
TRAY, RECT. "Primrose" (1959)	- 11"x6"	— 3.00
CUP, RECT. "Primrose" (1959)	- 5 oz.	— 1.50
TRAY, RECT., CRY. "Colonial Lady"	- 11"x6"	— 3.00
CUP, RECT., CRY. "Colonial Lady" (1960)	- 5 oz.	— 1.50
TRAY, OVAL, CRYSTAL "Vintage" (1960)	- 11¼"x6¼"	— 3.00
CUP, OVAL, CRYSTAL "Vintage" (1960)	- 5 oz.	— 1.50
TRAY, CRYSTAL, "Classic" (1960)	- 10 3/8"x6½"	— 3.00*
CUP, CRYSTAL, "Classic" (1960)	- 5 oz.	— 1.50*
TRAY, WHITE/GOLD TRIM "Classic"	- 10 3/8"x6½"	— 3.00
CUP, WHITE/GOLD TRIM "Classic"	- 5 oz.	— 1.50
PLATE, ROUND, CRYSTAL "Prescut"	- 10"	— 4.00
CUP, CRYSTAL "Prescut" (1961)	- 6 oz.	— 2.00
TRAY, RECT. "Wheat" (1962)	- 11"x6"	— 3.50
CUP, RECT. "Wheat" (1962)	- 5 oz.	— 1.50
PLATE, White/Gold Trim "Golden Shell"	- 10"	— 4.50
CUP, White/Gold Trim "Golden Shell" (1963)	- 8 oz.	— 3.00
TRAY, OVAL, WHITE, "Mosaic" (1966)	- 9¾"x7½"	— 3.50
CUP, STACKING, Blue/White	- 7½ oz.	— 3.00

Left To Right: Primrose, Fleuette, Wheat.

Left To Right: Blue Mosaic, Golden Shell, Milkwhite Classic.

Top Row: Crystal Serva-snack, Vintage, Colonial Lady. **Row 2:** Crystal Fan w/Royal Ruby Cup, Crystal Triangle w/Forest Green Cup, Crystal Fan w/Forest Green Cup.

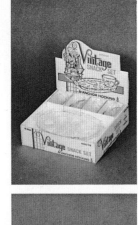

600/76

SNACK SETS

	CARTON		PRICE
GIFT PACKED	Sets	Lbs.	Set
600/76 8 pc. Vintage set. Four each 6 oz. cups and 11¼ x 6¾" trays. (004226)	4	31	$1.25
700/712 8 pc. Prescut set. Four each 6 oz. cups and 10" round snack plates. (004457)	4	38	1.60
W900/56 8 pc. Classic Milk-White set with 22K gold trim. Four each 5 oz. cups and 10⅜ x 6½" trays. (004820)	6	48	2.00
T4000/167 8 pc. Soreno Avocado set. Four each 7 oz. cups and 10" round snack plates. (018481)	4	29	1.60
W4600/79 8 pc. Blue Mosaic set. Four each 5 oz. cups and 9¾ x 7½" trays. (009225)	4	32	2.25

BULK PACKED	Doz.	Lbs.	Doz.
580 4 qt. punch/console bowl (004176)	½	27	6.30
588 6 qt. Swedish modern punch or salad bowl (013862)	½	31	9.00
586 5¼" salad/dessert (004184)	3	27	1.25
279 6 oz. punch cup (000315)	3	11	.85
260 5" Accent modern crystal bowl (020339)	3	21	1.25
262 9¼" Accent modern crystal bowl (020347)	1	29	4.20
589 6 oz. Swedish modern punch cup (013888)	3	14	1.20
585 5¼" Swedish modern salad bowl (017822)	3	25	1.45
587 8½" Swedish modern bowl (013854)	1	28	3.60

SALAD SET

	Sets	Lbs.	Set
500/98 3 pc. crystal clear set. Set contains 4 qt. bowl, lucite fork and spoon (004127)	4	21	1.10

CHIP & DIP SETS

	Sets	Lbs.	Set
500/90 3 pc. crystal clear set. Set contains 4 qt. bowl, 5¼" bowl, and brass finish holder. (004119)	4	23	1.10
J1259/241 3 pc. hand cut Forest Grove set in mailable carton. Set contains 5½" hand cut bowl, 8½" hand cut bowl, brass finish holder. (022046)	4	17	1.80
200/118 3 pc. crystal clear Accent modern set. Set contains 9¼" bowl, 5" bowl and brass frame. (020370)	4	14	1.00

700/712

W900/56

T4000/167

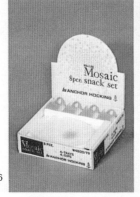

W4600/79

128

36

1968 Anchor Hocking Catalog

SERVA-SNACK SETS

W4000/17—8 Pce. Snack Set—22 K. Gold Trim

Each Set in Individual Die-Cut Display Style Gift Box,
6 Sets to Shipping Carton — 40 lbs.

COMPOSITION:
Four Cups—Ivory, 22 K. Gold Trimmed
Four Plates—Ivory, 22 K. Gold Trimmed

B4000/20—8 Pce. Snack Set—22 K. Gold Trim

Each Set in Individual Die-Cut Display Style Gift Box,
6 Sets to Shipping Carton — 41 lbs.

COMPOSITION:
Four Cups—Turquoise-Blue, 22 K. Gold Trimmed
Four Plates—Turquoise-Blue, 22 K. Gold Trimmed

THE ABOVE SETS ARE MADE OF HEAT-PROOF GLASS.

Cup is
Available
in
Open Stock

Sets are
Proven
Sales
Builders

200/78—8 Pce. Serva-Snack Set (Crystal Cups)

Each Set packed in a Pink Plaid Display Style Carton,
6 Sets to a Shipping Carton — 48 lbs.

COMPOSITION OF EACH SET: Four 5 oz. Cups
Four 11 x 6" Rectangular Trays

Directory on Page 2.

17.

Row 1: Fired On Pink Mug & Bowl, Fired On Yellow Mug & Bowl, Fired On Blue Mug & Bowl. **Row 2:** Ivory Mug & Bowl, 8 ½ Oz. Ivory Mug, 8 ½ Oz. Lustre Mug, Turquoise Blue Mug & Bowl. **Row 3:** Jade-ite Mug & Bowl, Jade-ite Shaving Mug, Ivory Shaving Mug, Anchorwhite Bowl & Mug.

Top Row: Ranger Mug, Cola Mug, Sunshine Mug, Blue Willow Mug, 5" Happy Home Bowl, BC Bowl, Desert Tone Bowl. **Row 2:** Day Breakers, Super Fruit, Sirloin Stockade Mug, Stuckey's Mug, Gail Clean Mug, Corning Mug, American Bicentenial Mug. **Row 3;** Footed Bowl, Footed Tulip Bowls, Snoopy Bowl, Stacking Soup Cup. **Row 4:** Kimberly Cups & Mugs, Mother of Pearl Mug & Bowl, Hot Color Bowl, 10½ oz. Diamond Mug. **Row 5:** Suburbia Mug & Bowl, Suburbia Mug & Bowls. **Row 6:** Sierra Mug, Calico Mugs, Concord, Pantry Blue Mug.

"MUGS AND BOWLS"
(1942-76)

The oldest mug is the "Sapphire Blue" ovenware mug with the "Philbe" design embossing, and there are two slightly different mugs. One heavy and one thin. The heavy mug has a smooth flat bottom, and was used as a shaving mug, where as the thin mug has a slightly raised ring on it's bottom, and was sold as a coffee mug. These same features also carry over to the older, plain jade-ite, and ivory mugs. We have found some of these flat bottomed mugs with the shaving soap, and sealed clear plastic lid still in tack. All of the "Philbe" embossed mugs we have found have the flat bottom of the shaving mug.

Most of the mugs came with a matching 5" cereal bowl, and were often sold as a set. These sets were made of almost every color Anchor Hocking used during this time period. There was, at this time, a very large market for these sets as premiums for everything from soap to flour, or as give-a-ways at gas stations, and grocery stores.

Then in the early 50's Anchor Hocking introduced the ivory "Davy Crocket" mug and bowl sets with two different style bowls, a 5" thin cereal, and a 4¾" tapered cereal bowl. Later they came out with the "Superman" and the "Batman and Robin" sets in both white and ivory, and several different colors of paint. A set called the "Prayer Set" used the white mug and bowl and red paint. The prayer on the mugs reads. "Bless this food, O Lord we pray, Make us strong from day to day." The bowl reads, "When I sleep or eat or play, God cares for me both night and day". About the time Exxon Oil Co. came out with the slogan "Put a tiger in your tank", they ordered a very large number of mug and bowl sets with the Exxon tiger on them. This is not the famed "Tony the Tiger" as many believed. In the late 60's the "Snoopy" set was introduced using a 9 oz. stacking mug, and a 5" flat, straight sided cereal bowl. In the mid 70's the "BC" cartoon bowl set came out using an unique style of bowls that resemble a turtle shell. These bowls have tab handles, and the "BC" cartoon characters on each side. This set consisted of a large serving bowl, and six cereal bowls.

In 1964 the "Kiddie Mealtime" set was introduced that consisted of a 7 oz. mug, a 6½" bowl, and a 7¼" plate. These have a rabbit and teddy bear on each piece. We have also found a 7½" divided child's plate in ivory with a blue trimmed edge.

There is a very popular set of late 60's stacking mugs and bowls with the "Blue Willow" design on anchorwhite. And a late 60's set with the "Game Birds" decals. There are many, many more sets of mugs and bowls, enough to fill a book on their own. We have listed the sets, and patterns that we have seen for sale in the flea markets, antique shops, malls, and the many glass shows we have traveled to over the years.

Top Row: Game Bird Mug, Game Bird Berry Bowl, Childs Dish, Kiddie Mealtime Mug. **Row 2:** Prayer Bowl, Prayer Mug, Exxon Tiger Mug, Exxon Tiger Bowl. **Row 3:** Davy Crockett Mugs & Bowls.

DESCRIPTION		CURRENT PRICES
CUP, Soup	- 5"	— $2.00
MUG, COLA	- 8 oz.	— 2.00
MUG, Ivory (Thin)	- 8 ½ oz.	— 6.00
MUG, Lustre (Thin)	- 8 ½ oz.	— 6.00
MUG, SAPPHIRE BLUE, HEAVY (Philbe)	- 8 oz.	— 18.00
MUG, SAPPHIRE BLUE, THIN (Philbe)	- 8 oz.	— 16.00
MUG, JADE-ITE, HEAVY (Philbe)	- 8 oz.	— 22.00
MUG, JADE-ITE, HEAVY, SHAVING	- 8 oz.	— 6.00
MUG, JADE-ITE, THIN	- 8 oz.	— 3.00
BOWL, JADE-ITE	- 5"	— 3.00
MUG, TURQUOISE BLUE	- 8 oz.	— 7.00
BOWL, TURQUOISE BLUE	- 5"	— 5.00
MUG, IVORY, SHAVING	- 8 oz.	— 6.00
MUG, IVORY, COFFEE	- 8 oz.	— 3.00
BOWL, IVORY	- 5"	— 3.00
MUG, WHITE	- 8 oz.	— 1.00
BOWL, WHITE	- 5"	— 1.00
MUG, FIRED ON COLORS	- 8 oz.	— 3.00
BOWL, FIRED ON COLORS	- 5"	— 3.00
Yellow, Turquoise, Coral, Sandalwood		
MUG, WHITE, DIAMONDS	- 10½ oz.	3.00
BOWL, WHITE, DIAMONDS	- 12½ oz.	3.00
Red, Yellow, Green, Turquoise Diamonds		
MUG, IVORY, DAVY CROCKET	- 8 oz.	— 15.00
BOWL, IVORY, DAVY CROCKET	- 5"	— 6.00
MUG, IVORY, DAVY CROCKET	- 8 oz.	— 17.00
BOWL, IVORY, BATMAN	- 5"	— 10.00
Blue, Red, Brown Print		
MUG, PRAYER RED PRINT	- 8 oz.	— 5.00
BOWL, PRAYER RED PRINT	- 5"	— 5.00
MUG, EXXON TIGER (White)	- 8 oz.	— 4.00
BOWL, EXXON TIGER (White)	- 5"	— 4.00
MUG, HAPPY HOME(Colors, 22K Rim)	- 8 oz.	— 2.00
BOWL, HAPPY HOME(Colors, 22K Rim)	- 5"	— 2.00
Yellow, Turquoise, Sandalwood, Coral		
MUG, PEACH LUSTRE (Copper Tint)	- 8 oz.	— 3.00
BOWL, PEACH LUSTRE (Copper Tint)	- 5"	— 3.00
BOWL, FOOTED, TULIP	- 4½"	— 4.00
Red, Blue, Green, Yellow, Purple, Pink Flowers		
MUG, Stacking (Mother of Pearl)	- 8 oz.	— 4.00
BOWL, FLAT BOTTOM (Mother of Pearl)	- 5"	— 4.50

3 PCE. KIDDIE MEALTIME SET

DESCRIPTION		CURRENT PRICES
MUG, RABBIT & TEDDY BEAR	- 7 oz.	— $3.00
BOWL, RABBIT & TEDDY BEAR	- 6½"	— 4.00
PLATE, RABBIT & TEDDY BEAR	- 7¼"	— 3.00
MUG, SIERRA, Stacking	- 9 oz.	— 2.00
BOWL, SIERRA, Stacking	- 5".	— 2.00
Mustard, Apricot, Red, Brownstone		
MUG, GOLDEN DIAMOND (Peach Lustre)	- 9 oz.	— 2.00
BOWL, GOLDEN DIAMOND FLAT BOTTOM	5"	— 2.00
MUG, MEADOW GREEN (Green Flowers)	- 9 oz.	— 2.00
BOWL, MEADOW GREEN (Green Flowers)	- 5"	— 2.00
MUG, KIMBERLY DIAMOND EMBOSSED	- 9 oz.	— 2.00
BOWL, KIMBERLY DIAMOND EMBOSSED	- 5"	— 2.00
White, Yellow/Maroon, L/D Blue, Yellow/Brown, L/D Green)		
MUG, DESSERT TONE (Stacking)	- 8 oz.	— 1.00
BOWL, DESSERT TONE	- 5"	— 1.00
Black and Sage / Dayberry / Nutmeg / Cinnamon)		
MUGS, LEISURE HOUR	- 8 oz.	— 1.00
ALPINE SPRING, DIAMOND POINT, TRELLIS ROSE,and MALABAR		
MUG, CAMELOT (Thumb Print, Stacking)	- 10 oz.	— 2.00
(Sage and Green / Blue / Black / Red)		
MUG, WILDLIFE	- 8 oz.	— 3.00
CANADA GOOSE, PHEASANT, RUFFLED GROUSE, MALLARD DUCK		
MUG, BLUE WILLOW (Stacking)	- 9 oz.	— 5.00
BOWL SET, B.C. TURTLE SHELL/Lg. SERVER		— 10.00
BOWL SET, B.C. TURTLE SHELL/Sm. CEREAL		— 3.00
MUG, SNOOPY (Stacking)	- 9 oz.	— 3.00
BOWL, SNOOPY, FLAT BOTTOM	- 5"	— 3.00

DAILY SIZZLING SELLERS

ALL NUMBERS ARE HEAT-PROOF

W384 — 9 oz. St. Denis Cup
Packs 4 doz.—24#
W327 — 5⅞" Saucer
Packs 4 doz.—21#

W383 — 8 oz. Ransom Cup
Packs 4 doz.—22#
W327 — 5⅞" Saucer
Packs 4 doz.—21#

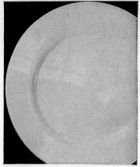

W341 — 9⅛" Dinner Plate
Packs 3 doz.—41#

COFFEE
MUGS
ARE VERY
FAST
SELLERS.

SOUP
BOWLS
TOO ARE
VERY
BIG.

W1212 — 8 oz. Coffee Mug
Packs 4 doz.—32#

W291 — 5" Soup or Cereal
Packs 4 doz.—30#

BOTH COLORS SELL WELL

G384 — 9 oz. St. Denis Cup
Packs 4 doz.—22#
G327 — 5⅞" Saucer
Packs 4 doz.—19#

G1212 — 8 oz. Coffee Mug
Packs 4 doz.—32#

G291 — 5" Soup or Cereal
Packs 4 doz.—31#

PROMOTE SETS FOR GREATER PROFITS

MUGS AND BOWLS — HEAT-PROOF

W1212/5931 — W1212/5932 — W1212/5933 — W1212/5934

W1212

W291

PACKING

W1212/5931—8 oz. Mug—Ruffed Grouse		4 doz. — 27 lbs.
W1212/5932—8 oz. Mug—Ring-Necked Pheasant		4 doz. — 27 lbs.
W1212/5933—8 oz. Mug—Canada Goose		4 doz. — 27 lbs.
W1212/5934—8 oz. Mug—Mallard Duck		4 doz. — 27 lbs.
W1212—8 oz. Coffee Mug		4 doz. — 27 lbs.
W291—5" Soup or Cereal		4 doz. — 29 lbs.

W64

G1212

G291

G384 — G327

W64—4¾" Basket Weave Bowl	4 doz. — 24 lbs.
G1212—8 oz. Coffee Mug	4 doz. — 29 lbs.
G291—5" Soup or Cereal	4 doz. — 30 lbs.
G384—9 oz. St. Denis Cup	4 doz. — 24 lbs.
G327—5⅞" Saucer	4 doz. — 23 lbs.

See Page 6 for Jade-ite Dinnerware and Page 54 for Jade-ite Mixing Bowls.

B1212

B291

L1212

L291

B1212—8 oz. Coffee Mug	4 doz. — 24 lbs.
B291—5" Soup or Cereal	4 doz. — 27 lbs.
L1212—8 oz. Coffee Mug	4 doz. — 29 lbs.
L291—5" Soup or Cereal	4 doz. — 29 lbs.

Blue Dinnerware is on Page 5, Ash Trays on Page 32 and Mixing Bowls on Page 53.

For a Complete Line of Peach Lustre Dinnerware see Page 7.

9.

MUGS AND BOWLS - FOUR COLORS - HEAT-PROOF

G1212

G291

W1212

W291

PACKING

G1212—8 oz. Coffee Mug	4 doz. — 27 lbs.
G291—5" Soup or Cereal	4 doz. — 28 lbs.
W1212—8 oz. Coffee Mug	4 doz. — 27 lbs.
W291—5" Soup or Cereal	4 doz. — 28 lbs.

See Jade-ite Tableware on Page 20.   Ivory Tableware is shown on Page 22.

L1212

L291

B1212

B291

L1212—8 oz. Coffee Mug	4 doz. — 26 lbs.
L291—5" Soup or Cereal	4 doz. — 27 lbs.
B1212—8 oz. Coffee Mug	4 doz. — 27 lbs.
B291—5" Soup or Cereal	4 doz. — 28 lbs.

Peach Lustre Tableware Line is shown on Page 21.   Turquoise-Blue Tableware Line is shown on Page 18.

DECORATED BOWLS

13-Ounce
Cereal
Bowls

Tulip
Decoration

W130/1740—13 oz. Cereal Bowl—Green	3 doz. — 19 lbs.
W130/1741—13 oz. Cereal Bowl—Red	3 doz. — 19 lbs.
W130/1742—13 oz. Cereal Bowl—Turquoise	3 doz. — 19 lbs.
W130/1743—13 oz. Cereal Bowl—Yellow	3 doz. — 19 lbs.

THE ABOVE BOWLS HAVE A DESIGN OF SIMPLICITY AND BEAUTY WITH EVERYDAY
USEFULNESS FOR BREAKFAST CEREALS, LUNCHEON SOUPS AND SALADS.

23.

happy home mugs and bowls

Satin tint colors on milk-white. Rimmed in 22K gold.

W1212/6351   W1212/6352   W1212/6353   W1212/6354

8 oz. Coffee Mugs		Doz. Ctn.	Lbs. Ctn.
W1212/6351	coral	2	14
W1212/6352	turquoise	2	14
W1212/6353	yellow	2	14
W1212/6354	sandalwood	2	14

5" Bowls			Doz. Ctn.	Lbs. Ctn.
W291/6351		coral	2	15
W291/6352		turquoise	2	15
W291/6353		yellow	2	15
W291/6354		sandalwood	2	15
W1212	8 oz	Anchorwhite mug	2	14
W291	5"	Anchorwhite soup/cereal	2	15
G1212	8 oz	Jade-ite mug	2	14
G291	5"	Jade-ite soup/cereal	2	15
L1212	8 oz	Peach Lustre mug	2	14
L291	5"	Peach Lustre soup/cereal	2	15

W291/6351   W291/6352   W291/6353   W291/6354

W327   W384   W291   W1212   L1212   L291

Carry-Out Pack		Sets Ctn.	Lbs. Ctn.
4 pc sets			
W1212-Q	Anchorwhite mug	12	29

St. Denis Cups/Saucers			Doz. Ctn.	Lbs. Ctn.
W384	9 oz	Anchorwhite cup	3	16
W327	5⅞"	Anchorwhite saucer	3	15
G384	9 oz	Jade-ite cup	3	16
G327	5⅞"	Jade-ite saucer	3	15

G291   G1212   G384   G327

3 Pc Kiddie Mealtime Set		Sets Ctn.	Lbs. Ctn.
W4600/60	gift display carton, one each 7¼" plate, 6½" cereal bowl, and 7 oz mug	6	14

W4600/60

59

5" SOUP OR CEREAL BOWLS	CARTON	
(heat resistant)	Doz.	Lbs.
W310/6514 maroon (038885)	2	13
W310/6516 green (038893)	2	13
W310/6517 orange (038901)	2	13
W310/6519 yellow (038919)	2	13

MUGS AND BOWLS (heat resistant)

	Doz.	Lbs.
W2378 8½" bowl (005322)	1	14
L2369 3¼ oz. lustre shell demitasse cup (017939)	6	18
L2339 4¾" lustre shell demitasse saucer (017947)	6	16
W2369 3¼ oz. Anchorwhite demitasse cup (017962)	6	18
W2339 4¾" Anchorwhite demitasse saucer (017970)	6	16
L291 5" peach lustre bowl (003798)	2	15
L1212 8 oz. peach lustre mug (004986)	2	14
W1212 8 oz. Anchorwhite mug (004994)	2	14
W291 5" Anchorwhite bowl (003806)	2	15

CANDLEGLOW

W310/73 5" bowl (019984)	2	16
W312/73 8 oz. stacking mug (019976)	2	13
ANCHOR PACKS (Sets of 4)	Sets	Lbs.
W1212-D 8 oz. white mug (008888)	12	28

MUGS AND BOWLS	CARTON	
(heat resistant)	Doz.	Lbs.
W312/6766 8 oz. Aurora sprayed mug (030643)	2	13
W310/6766 5" Aurora sprayed bowl (030650)	2	16
L312 8 oz. coppertint mug (030668)	2	13
L310 5" coppertint bowl (031005)	2	16
W312 8 oz. milk white mug (017954)	2	13
W310 5" soup or cereal bowl (019968)	2	16

DESERT TONE CONTINENTAL

MUGS (heat resistant)

W314/6772 10½ oz. ceramic sprayed mugs in assorted decorations. Assortment consists of bayberry and black, sage and black, cinnamon and black and nutmeg and black. (088260)	2	18

BULK PACKED

W314 10½ oz. white (075127)	2	18
W314/6768 10½ oz. bayberry and black mug (075135)	2	18
W314/6769 10½ oz. sage and black mug (075143)	2	18
W314/6770 10½ oz. cinnamon and black mug (075150)	2	18
W314/6771 10½ oz. nutmeg and black mug (074831)	2	18

Back Row: Jade-ite Plain, Royal Lustre, Jane-Ray Lustre, Lustre Shell. **Center Row:** Ivory Plain, Royal White, Jane-Ray Jade-ite, Golden Shell.
Front Row: Standard size Jane-Ray Cup & Saucer, Jane-Ray White W/Gold Trim, White Shell.

"DEMITASSE"
(1960's)

The "Demitasse" cup and saucer sets were developed by Anchor Hocking in the 60's for the expresso coffee market that was the rage of that time. A lot of people have collected these sets thinking they were part of a child's set of dishes. The trouble with this theory, Anchor Hocking never made a child's tableware set during this time period.

The trademarks found on these are, (OVEN Fire-King WARE MADE IN U.S.A.), (ANCHOR HOCKING OVEN Fire-King WARE MADE IN U.S.A.), and (ANCHOR HOCKING [anchor over H symbol] Fire-King OVEN-PROOF, mold number, MADE IN U.S.A.). The plain jade-ite and ivory sets are not trademarked.

The hard to find pieces are the "Jane Ray" pattern in jade-ite which fetches a higher price than the lustre, or white/gold trim sets in the same pattern.

PRICE GUIDE

DESCRIPTION		CURRENT PRICES			
		JADE-ITE	LUSTRE	WHITE/G	IVORY
CUP, "Jane Ray"	- 3½ oz.	- $12.00	- $5.00	- $5.00	- $ N/A
SAUCER, "Jane Ray"	- 4½"	- 7.00	- 3.00	- 3.00	- N/A
CUP, (Plain)	- 3 oz.	- 5.00	- 5.00	- N/A	- 5.00
SAUCER, (Plain)	- 4½"	- 2.00	- N/A	- N/A	- 2.00
CUP, "Shell"	- 3¼ oz.	- 4.00	- 3.00	- 3.00	- N/A
SAUCER, "Shell"	-4¾"	- 2.00	- 1.00	- 1.00	- N/A
CUP, (Royal)	- 3¼ oz.	- N/A	- 3.00	- 3.00*	- N/A
SAUCER, (Royal)	- 4¾"	- N/A	- 2.00	- 2.00*	- N/A
CUP, (Fish Scale)	- 3¼ oz.	- N/A	- 5.00	- 4.00*	- N/A**
SAUCER, (Fish Scale)	- 4¾"	- N/A	- 2.00	- 2.00*	- N/A**

*White without the gold trim.
**Not Pictured

"FRENCH CASSEROLE"
(1958-1976)
COPPER TINT, WHITE

The ribbed casseroles came with clear glass lids, packed in 8 pc. and 16 pc. sets. While the smooth sided casserole came with plastic lids only. The metal lids were used mostly for advertisements, such as "FARMERS DAIRY COTTAGE CHEESE", "PURE PORK COUNTRY SAUSAGE", and "ELM HILL MEATS". These were premium offers for free "FIRE-KING" ovenware glass bowls. By the way, these bowls are great in the microwave as well as the oven. They make great chili or soup bowls, because when they come out of the microwave they have a nice cool handle.

PRICE GUIDE

DESCRIPTION	CURRENT PRICES	
CASSEROLE, RIBBED (Clear Tab Lid)	- 12 oz.	- $6.00
CASSEROLE, RIBBED (Metal Lid)	- 12 oz.	- 5.00
CASSEROLE, SMOOTH SIDE (Plastic Lid)	- 12 oz.	- 4.00

NOTE: Casserole without lid deduct $1.00.

Top Row: 13 oz. Ice Tea Tumbler, 10 oz. Roly Poly, 9 oz. Roly Poly, Footed Sugar, Footed Creamer, Footed Sherbert, Footed Juice Tumbler, Footed Goblet Tumbler. **Row 2:** 80 oz. Whirley Twirley, Harding Vase, Coolidge Vase, Wilson Ivy Ball, 20 oz. Tilt. **Row 3:** Medium Ashtray, Small Ashtray, Flat Sugar, Flat Creamer, Marmalade Jar and Lid, Maple Leaf Bowl, 10 hr. Candle Cup, 15 hr. Candle Cup.

Top Row: Bubble Sugar and Creamer, 9 oz. Flared Tumbler, Handled Tumbler, Sherbert Plate, 5 oz. Roly Poly Juice, 9 oz. Roly Poly Tabler Tumbler, 9 oz. Whirley Twirley Tumbler, Polka Dot Ice Tea. **Row 2:** 3 qt. Water Pitcher, 22 oz. Juice Pitcher, Roosevelt Vase, 3¾″ Flared Top Flower Vase, Coolidge Vase, Harding Vase. **Row 3:** Batter Bowl, 5⅝″ Splash Proof Bowl, 5″ Bowl, 5″ Ribbed Bowl, 6″ Ribbed Bowl. **Row 4:** Leaf & Blossum, Maple Leaf, 3½″ Ashtray, 4⅝″ Ashtray, 5⅜″ Ashtray, Sherbert (Boopie).

"ROYAL RUBY" ACCESSORY ITEMS
(1940-1964)
"FOREST GREEN" ACCESSORY ITEMS
(1953-1976)

The royal ruby color glass was used to produce four tableware sets, R1700 (flat), R2200 "Charm" (square), R1600 "Bubble" and the R4000 (same style as the "Turquoise Blue" tableware). There was also a very large number of accessory items produced in the royal ruby color. We will try to list as many as we have information on or have found to have been made by Anchor Hocking.

The forest green color glassware was used to produce two tableware sets, "Charm" (square) and "Bubble". These patterns were produced in several colors. So for now we'll cover the accessory pieces of forest green.

Anchor Hocking very rarely embossed this glass with its trademark. You can find some tumblers marked with the anchor over H symbol but most pieces came with labels instead, which read (ROYAL RUBY ANCHORGLASS Anchor Hocking Glass Corp. Lancaster Ohio, U.S.A.) or (FOREST GREEN ANCHORGLASS Anchor Hocking Glass Corp. Lancaster Ohio, U.S.A.).

PRICE GUIDE

DESCRIPTION		R/R	F/G
TUMBLER, Juice (Roly Poly)	- 5 oz.	5.00	$4.50
TUMBLER, Table (Roly Poly)	- 9 oz.	7.00	6.00
TUMBLER, Iced Tea (Roly Poly)	- 13 oz.	11.00	10.00
PITCHER, Water	- 3 qt.	45.00	38.00
PITCHER, Juice	- 22 oz.	25.00	15.00
TUMBLER, Footed, Juice	- 5 oz.	5.00	4.00
TUMBLER, Footed, Goblet	- 10 oz.	6.00	5.00
COCKTAIL, Footed	- 3½ oz.	4.50	3.50
BOWL, Sherbet, (Footed)	- 6½ oz.	6.00	4.00
PLATE, Sherbet, (Footed)	- 6¼"	5.00	4.00
PITCHER, BALL (Tilted)	- 42 oz.	55.00	40.00
PITCHER, BALL (Tilted)	- 22 oz.	28.00	24.00
TUMBLER, Footed Wine	- 2½"	12.00	N/A
TUMBLER, Flared	- 9 oz.	4.00	3.00
TUMBLER, Straight Side	- 11 oz.	5.00	4.00
TUMBLER, Straight Side Iced Tea	- 15 oz.	6.00	5.00
TUMBLER, Straight Side Iced Tea	- 22 oz.	9.00	8.00
TUMBLER, Georgian	- 9 oz.	8.00	6.00
TUMBLER, HANDLED	- 4 5/8"	N/A	10.00
PITCHER, Ice Lip	- 80 oz.	55.00	40.00
PITCHER, Milano	- 3 qt.	N/A	40.00
TUMBLER, Milano	- 5 oz.	N/A	3.00
TUMBLER, Milano	- 7 oz.	N/A	4.00
TUMBLER, Milano	- 12 oz.	N/A	5.00
TUMBLER, Milano	- 15 oz.	N/A	5.50
TUMBLER, Long Boy Iced Tea	- 16 oz.	N/A	8.00
TUMBLER, Giant Iced Tea	- 32 oz.	12.00	10.00
MIXING BOWL	- 6"	N/A	5.00
SPLASH-PROOF BOWL	- 5 5/8"	N/A	6.00
BATTER BOWL	- 7 5/8"	N/A	14.00
ASHTRAY, Square	- 5¾"	8.00	6.00
ASHTRAY, Square	- 4 5/8"	7.00	5.00
ASHTRAY, Square	- 3½"	6.00	4.00
ASHTRAY, Hexagonal	- 5¾"	10.00	8.00
ASHTRAY, Coaster	- 3¼"	N/A	4.00
JAR, Marmalade, Lid		10.00	N/A

PRICE GUIDE

DESCRIPTION		R/R	F/G
ASHTRAY, Grape Cluster	- 4½"	6.50	$N/A
VASE, Ivy Ball (Footed)	- 4¾"	6.50	4.50
VASE, WILSON (Ivy Ball)	- 4"	5.00	4.00
VASE, HARDING	- 6 3/8"	6.50	4.50
VASE, COOLIDGE	- 6 3/8"	6.50	4.50
VASE, HOOVER	- 9"	15.00	10.00
VASE, ROOSEVELT (Gold Bands)	- 3¾"	6.00	4.00
VASE, BUD	- 3¾"	6.00	4.00
VASE, Crimped Top	- 7"	9.00	7.00
VASE, Crimped Top	- 6½"	8.00	6.00
VASE, Flared Top	- 9"	12.00	8.00
VASE, BALL (Mosquito Repellent)	- 4"	5.00	4.00
VASE, PANELED	- 9"	N/A	11.00
VASE, BUD TALL	- 9"	N/A	4.00
PLATE, (Leaf & Blossom)	- 8¼"	N/A	6.00
BOWL, (Leaf & Blossom)	- 4½"	N/A	5.00
PUNCH BOWL / STAND (4 qt.)	- 10¼"	50.00	30.00
PUNCH CUP	- 5 oz.	4.00	3.00
MAPLE LEAF BOWL	- 6 5/8"l	6.50	4.50
BOWL, Flared	- 5"	N/A	4.00
BOWL, Ribbed	- 5"	N/A	5.00
BOWL, Oyster & Pearl	- 8½"	N/A	12.00
BOWL, Oyster & Pearl	- 4 5/8"	N/A	4.00
CANDLE TUMBLER	- 10 hr.	3.50	2.00
CANDLE TUMBLER	- 15 hr.	3.50	2.00
STEMWARE, Cocktail "Boopie"	- 3½ oz.	6.50	4.50
STEMWARE, Sherbet "Boopie"	- 6 oz.	7.50	5.50
STEMWARE, Juice or Wine "Boopie"	- 4 oz.	8.50	6.50
STEMWARE, Goblet "Boopie"	- 9 oz.	12.50	10.00
STEMWARE, Ice Tea "Boopie"	- 15 oz.	16.50	14.00
BOWL, 3-Cornered Bonbon	- 6¼"	N/A	5.00
BOWL, Scalloped	- 6½"	N/A	6.00
BOWL, Crimped	- 7½"	N/A	8.00
TRAY, Handled Relish	- 8¼"	N/A	10.00
APOTHECARY JAR & COVER	- 24 oz.	9.00	N/A
RELISH SET, Service Plate	- 14"	N/A	25.00
RELISH SET, Sauce Dish	- 4"	N/A	4.00

FOREST GREEN GIFT ITEMS

1956 Catalog

E159

E5069

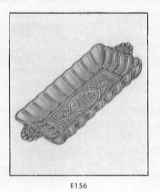

E156

E55

		PACKING
E159—6 ¼ ″ 3-Cornered Bonbon		4 doz. — 32 lbs.
E5069—6 ½ ″ Scalloped Bowl		4 doz. — 35 lbs.
E156—8 ¼ ″ Handled Relish Tray		4 doz. — 42 lbs.
E55—7 ½ ″ Crimped Bowl		2 doz. — 26 lbs.

DESSERT SERVICE   BOWLS

E1874

E1878

E356 — E357

E365

E1874—4 ⅝ ″ Fruit	6 doz. — 26 lbs.
E1878—8 ½ ″ Bowl	2 doz. — 39 lbs.
E356—6″ Mixing Bowl	3 doz. — 34 lbs.
E357—7 ¼ ″ Mixing Bowl	2 doz. — 34 lbs.
E365—5 ⅝ ″ Splash-Proof Bowl	3 doz. — 37 lbs.

TUMBLERS   PITCHERS

E3653 — E3651

E3658

E86

E1946

E3653— 5 oz. Fruit Juice	6 doz. — 16 lbs.
E3651— 9 oz. Table Tumbler	6 doz. — 26 lbs.
E3658—13 oz. Iced Tea	6 doz. — 31 lbs.
E86—86 oz. Ice Lip Pitcher	1 doz. — 32 lbs.
E1946—36 oz. Pitcher	1 doz. — 22 lbs.

Forest Green Vases are listed on Page 41.

30.

FOREST GREEN Anchorglass ®

E3653

E3651 — E3658

E86

E71

PACKING

E3653— 5 oz. Fruit Juice		6 doz. — 16 lbs.
E3651— 9 oz. Table Tumbler		6 doz. — 26 lbs.
E3658—13 oz. Iced Tea		6 doz. — 31 lbs.
E86—86 oz. Ice Lip Pitcher		1 doz. — 34 lbs.
E71— 9 oz. Tumbler		6 doz. — 33 lbs.

Roly-Poly Line in Crystal Glass shown on Page 9.

E3597

E65 — E69

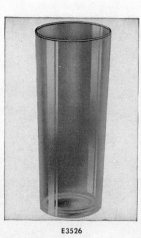

E3526

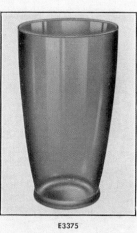

E3375

E3597— 9½ oz. Tall Tumbler		6 doz. — 29 lbs.
E65—11 oz. Tumbler		6 doz. — 28 lbs.
E69—15 oz. Tall Iced Tea		6 doz. — 39 lbs.
E3526—15 oz. Long Boy Iced Tea		6 doz. — 38 lbs.
E3375—32 oz. Giant Iced Tea		2 doz. — 20 lbs.

E356

E365

E761

E236

E356—6"	Mixing Bowl		3 doz. — 34 lbs.
E365—5⅝"	Splash-Proof Bowl		3 doz. — 37 lbs.
E761—5"	Bowl		4 doz. — 25 lbs.
E236—5"	Bowl		4 doz. — 25 lbs.

46.

DECORATED LINE

(Blown)

LEAF
DESIGN
IN
WHITE ENAMEL

PACKING

E65/351—11 oz. Tumbler	6 doz. — 25 lbs.
E69/351—15 oz. Iced Tea	6 doz. — 38 lbs.
E93/351—22 oz. Giant Iced Tea	3 doz. — 26 lbs.
E86/351—86 oz. Ice Lip Pitcher	1 doz. — 33 lbs.

POLKA DOTS
IN
WHITE ENAMEL

E65/352—11 oz. Tumbler	6 doz. — 25 lbs.
E69/352—15 oz. Iced Tea	6 doz. — 38 lbs.
E93/352—22 oz. Giant Iced Tea	3 doz. — 26 lbs.
E86/352—86 oz. Ice Lip Pitcher	1 doz. — 33 lbs.

1954 Anchor Hocking Catalog

A1031—10 oz. Tumbler
6 doz. ctn.—48 lbs.

A1087—80 oz. Jug
1 doz. ctn.—34 lbs.

E514—3⅝"x5⅛" Crystal Marmalade—With Ruby Cover
2 doz. ctn.—22 lbs.

A4474—4½" Dessert Nappy
6 doz. ctn.—23 lbs.

12   **ANCHOR HOCKING GLASS CORPORATION** HOCKING DIVISION

VASES — FOREST GREEN AND RUBY

★ E3302

★ R3302

☆ E3345

☆ R3345

	COST DOZ.	PACKING
★ E3302—3¾″ Forest Green Bud Vase	.60	4 doz. — 18 lbs.
★ R3302—3¾″ Ruby Bud Vase	.60	4 doz. — 17 lbs.
★ E3345—6⅜″ Forest Green Vase	.70	4 doz. — 35 lbs.
☆ R3345—6⅜″ Ruby Vase	.70	4 doz. — 33 lbs.

★ E3346

☆ R3346

E3306

E3308

★ E3346—6⅜″ Forest Green Vase	.70	4 doz. — 33 lbs.
★ R3346—6⅜″ Ruby Vase	.70	4 doz. — 33 lbs.
E3306—6½″ Crimped Top Vase	.65	4 doz. — 22 lbs.
E3308—7″ Crimped Top Vase	1.20	2 doz. — 23 lbs.

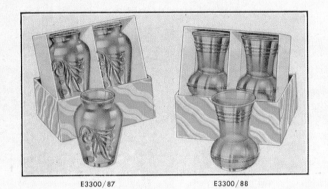
E3300/87   E3300/88

★ 1071

☆ 3354

E3300/87—2 Pce. Forest Green Bud Vase Set—Gold Dec.	.22 Set	24 Sets — 20 lbs.
(Each Set in Gift Box)		
COMP.: Two Forest Green Vases—Gold Dec.		
E3300/88—2 Pce. Forest Green Bud Vase Set—Gold Bands	.22 Set	24 Sets — 21 lbs.
(Each Set in Gift Box)		
COMP.: Two Forest Green Vases—Gold Bands		
★ 1071—9″ Bud Vase	.65	4 doz. — 39 lbs.
★ 3354—4″ Ivy Ball	.60	4 doz. — 22 lbs.

PRINTED IN U.S.A.

Listing with ANCHOR HOCKING GLASS CORP., Lancaster, Ohio, U. S. A.   **31.**

R1606

R1600/55—9 Pce. Refreshment Set
Each Set in Printed Parchment Box,
4 Sets to Shipping Carton — 31 lbs.
COMPOSITION:
Eight R1612 Tumblers
One R1660 Pitcher

R1600/56—24 Pce. Hostess Service Set
Each Set in Printed Parchment
Carton — 12 lbs.
COMPOSITION:
Eight R1606 Juice Glasses
Eight R1612 Tumblers
Eight R1616 Iced Teas

R1609

PACKING

R1606—6 oz. Fruit Juice .... 3 doz. — 10 lbs.
R1609—9 oz. Old Fashioned .... 3 doz. — 15 lbs.

See Page 21 for Luncheon Sets in Royal Ruby.

R1612 — R1616

R1600/57—25 Pce. Refreshment Set
Each Set in Printed Parchment
Carton — 16 lbs.
COMPOSITION:
Eight R1606 Juice Glasses
Eight R1612 Tumblers
Eight R1616 Iced Teas
One R1660 Pitcher

R1600/58—24 Pce. Hostess Service Set
Each Set in Printed Parchment
Carton — 12 lbs.
COMPOSITION:
Six R1606 Juice Glasses
Six R1609 Old Fashioneds
Six R1612 Tumblers
Six R1616 Iced Teas

R1660

R1612—12 oz. Tumbler .... 3 doz. — 18 lbs.
R1616—16 oz. Iced Tea .... 3 doz. — 22 lbs.
R1660—64 oz. Ice Lip Pitcher .... ½ doz. — 17 lbs.

ROLY POLY TUMBLERS

R3653 — R3651

R3600/455—18 Pce. Hostess Service Set
Each Set in Printed Parchment
Carton — 6 lbs.
COMPOSITION:
Six R3653 Juice Glasses
Six R3651 Tumblers
Six R3658 Iced Teas

R3658

R3653— 5 oz. Fruit Juice .... 6 doz. — 16 lbs.
R3651— 9 oz. Table Tumbler .... 6 doz. — 24 lbs.
R3658—13 oz. Iced Tea .... 6 doz. — 30 lbs.

See Page 67 for Royal Ruby Ash Trays and Page 69 for Royal Ruby Vases.

35.

E4005 — E4012 — E4015

E4007

E4087

PACKING

E4005	— 5 oz. Heavy Base Tumbler	3 doz. — 12 lbs.
E4007	— 7 oz. Heavy Base Old Fashioned	3 doz. — 17 lbs.
E4012	—12 oz. Heavy Base Tumbler	3 doz. — 23 lbs.
E4015	—15 oz. Heavy Base Tumbler	3 doz. — 25 lbs.
E4087	— 3 Qt. Ice Lip Pitcher	½ doz. — 20 lbs.
E4000/61	— 9 Pce. Refreshment Set	4 sets — 32 lbs.

(Each Set in Parchment Gift Box)

COMPOSITION: Eight E4012 Tumblers and one E4087 Pitcher

E3526

PITCHER

E3587

E3526	—16 oz. Long Boy Iced Tea	3 doz. — 20 lbs.
E3587	— 3 Qt. Pitcher	½ doz. — 20 lbs.

MILK WHITE

W553

W500/55—7 Pce. Water Set
Each Set in Gift Carton,
6 Sets to Shipping Carton — 43 lbs.
COMPOSITION:
    One W548 Pitcher
    Six W553 Tumbler

W548

W553	— 9 oz. Water Tumbler	3 doz. — 21 lbs.
W548	—72 oz. Pitcher	½ doz. — 19 lbs.

37.

Top Row: Bud Vase, 4" Jardiniere, 4" Jardiniere, 5" Jardeniere, 9½" Vase. **Row 2:** Cookie Jar & Lid, 9 oz. Tumbler, 10 oz. Goblet, 10 oz. Goblet, 18 oz. Pitcher, 72 oz. Pitcher.

Top Row: Square Flat Ashtray, Milkwhite Ashtray, Hobnail Cloverleaf Dish, Hobnail Candy Dish, (no cover), Flower Pot. **Row 2:** Candle Cup, Footed Sherbert, Golf Ball, Base Ball, 9½ x 5½ Planter, Covered Candy Dish. **Row 3:** 8½ sq. Footed Bowl, Candle Holder, 12 oz. Milk Pitcher, 6½" Square Bowl. **Row 4:** Vintage Footed Candy Jar & Lid, Vintage Footed Candy Jar (no lid), 10" Vintage Footed Bowl, Footed Planter, 7¼" Vase.

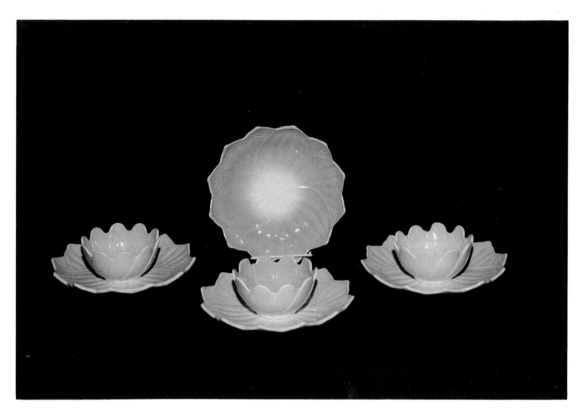

Leaf & Blossom

Top Row: Tall Ribbed Lustre Vase, Deco Vases, Smooth Ivory Flower Pot, Maple Leaves. **Row 2:** Leaf & Blossom Sets. **Row 3:** 6 ½" Lustre "Bibi" Bowl, Jade-Ite Bowl, Sea Shell Bowls, Lustre Tulip Ash Tray. **Row 4:** 4 ¼" Ash Tray, Rose Top Cigarette Box, Ruffled Flower Pot, Scalloped Flower Pot, Footed Bulb Bowl, Ruffle Rim Bowl. **Row 5:** 2 Sport Jade-ite Skillet, 1 Sport Jade-ite Skillet, Jade-ite Fancy Bowl, Footed Candy Dish, Smooth Jade-ite Flower Pot.

"FIRE-KING NOVELTIES"
(1940-1976)

Anchor Hocking produced a very large line of novelty items during the "FIRE-KING" years. These novelties were made in almost every color Anchor Hocking used during this period of time. It seems that every time we are out looking for "FIRE-KING" glassware we find something we have never seen before. Not all the novelties will have the "FIRE-KING" trademarks, but the distinctive Anchor Hocking colors will give them away every time.

There are two common Jade-ite skillets, the one spout and the two spout, both measure 6¼". But while at Anchor Hocking's glassware morgue Phil Bee showed us two smaller Jade-ite skillets which we had never seen anywhere else.

The "Deco" 5" vase is often found in jade-ite but was also made in opaque blue and vitrock with several fired on pastel colors. The "Leaf & Blossom" sets were made in almost every Anchor Hocking color. There is a similar set to the "Leaf and Blossom". The difference being the rim of the bowl has been flared and the plate is smaller with rounded leaves. The "Rose Top" cigarette box was made in jade-ite, crystal, royal ruby and some fired on colors. These boxes came with matching 4¼" square ashtrays.

The fancy bowls, or "Bullseye" bowls as Anchor Hocking called them, were made in several colors. The flat candy dish can be found in all of the "FIRE-KING" colors plus several fired-on colors. A 10" crystal "Bullseye" (bubble) sandwich plate was sold separately from the tableware sets. The two different Hurricane lamps, are the same size but have different bases. One base has several columns of beads while the other has straight columns with a bead on top and bottom of each column. There is a two piece "Baseball" set, and a two piece "Golfball" set in milk white, as well as a two piece "Football" set in the dark amber glass. These are marked with the anchor over H symbol. There are two different sets of milk-white bubble bowls, one consists of six 4" berry bowls and one 8" serving bowl and the other has six 5" cereal bowls and one 11" serving bowl. The maple leaf and the sea shell were made in all of the "Fire-King" colors.

There are three different flower pots, the 3½" smooth rim, the 3½" scalloped rim and the 4½" ruffled rimmed. These pots can be found in jade-ite, ivory and several fired on colors. We have only found the footed bulb bowl in jade-ite but there should be other colors. There's several pieces of milk-white hobnail, a large and small pitcher, three different glasses (two footed and one flat), three vases (one footed with a ruffled rim, and a large and a small scalloped rim flat vase), and a cookie jar with a lid. Some of the hobnail pieces will have the "FIRE-KING" trademarks but most are marked with only the mold number.

There were many more novelties that were made during the "FIRE-KING" years than we have listed here. These are a few we thought would be of interest. As time goes on, we hope to add more to this list and cover them in more detail.

PRICE GUIDE

DESCRIPTION		CURRENT PRICES
"JADE-ITE"		
SKILLET, (One Spout)	- 6 ¼"	$20.00
VASE, DECO	- 5"	5.00
SKILLET, (Two Spout)	- 6 ¼"	25.00
SEA SHELL*	- 6 ½"	4.00
MAPLE LEAF	- 6 5/8"	3.00
CANDY DISH (Flat/Knob Lid)	- 6 ¾"	10.00
CANDY DISH, Footed,		
Scalloped Rim	- 6"	8.00
BOWL, Flat	- 5"	3.00
BOWL, Diamond Bottom	- 6"	6.00
BOWL, (Ruffled Rim)	- 7 5/8"	8.00
BOWL, FANCY "Bubble"	- 8 ½"	8.00
CIGARETTE BOX (Rose Top)*	- 3½"x4½"	22.00
ASH TRAY	- 4 ¼"	4.50
POT, FLOWER (Scalloped Rim)	- 3 ½"	4.50
POT, FLOWER (Smooth Rim)	- 3 ½"	4.50
POT, FLOWER (Ruffled Rim)	- 4 ½"	5.00
BOWL, BULB, Footed	- 5 ¼"	5.00
CUP, DESSERT "Leaf & Blossom"#	- 4 ¾"	4.00
PLATE, "Leaf & Blossom"#	- 8"	4.00

*-(DEDUCT $1.00 FOR MILK-WHITE OR ADD $3.00 FOR ROYAL RUBY)

#-(DEDUCT $1.00 FOR CRYSTAL OR ADD $2.00 FOR AZUR-ITE)

DESCRIPTION		CURRENT PRICES
"CRYSTAL"		
CIGARETTE BOX/LID	- 4 3/8"	7.00
ASH TRAY	- 3 3/4"	1.00
BOWL, SERVING (Crystal Sandwich)	- 8 ½"	8.00
BOWL, DESSERT (Crystal Sandwich)	- 4 ½"	4.50
LEAF DESSERT SET, BOWL	- 8 ½"	10.00
LEAF DESSERT SET, DESSERT	- 5 ¼"	5.00
BOWL, BULLSEYE Crystal "Bubble"	- 8 3/8"	5.00
PLATE, BULLSEYE Crystal "Bubble"	- 10"	10.00
LAMP, HURRICANE (Crystal) 2 pc.	- 7"	8.00
DISH, BUTTER (Crystal) 2 pc.	- 7¼"x2¾"	4.50

PRICE GUIDE

DESCRIPTION		CURRENT PRICES
SHAKERS, SALT (Crystal/Tulip Lid)	- 4 ¾"	$3.00
SHAKERS, PEPPER (Crystal/Tulip Lid)	- 4 ¼"	3.00
SHAKERS, SALT (Aluminum Top)	- 3 ¼"	1.50
SHAKERS, PEPPER (Aluminum Top)	- 3 ¼"	1.50
SHAKERS, SALT (Aluminum Top)	- 4 ¼"	2.00
SHAKERS, PEPPER (Aluminum Top)	- 4 ¼"	2.00
SHAKERS, SALT (Chrome Top)	- 2 ¾"	2.50
SHAKERS, PEPPER (Chrome Top)	- 2 ¾"	2.50
SHAKERS, SALT (Chrome Top)	- 4"	3.00
SHAKERS, PEPPER (Chrome Top)	- 4"	3.00
SHAKERS, SALT (RED Plastic Top)	- 3 ½"	1.50
SHAKERS, PEPPER (RED Plastic Top)	- 3 ½"	1.50
MEASURING CUP, 3 Spout	- 8 oz	4.00
WATER BOTTLE/Metal Cap	- 1 qt.	8.00
WATER BOTTLE/Metal Cap	- 2 qt.	10.00
CRUET/STOPPER	- 5 oz.	4.00
CRUET/STOPPER	- 6 ¼"	6.00
JUICER	- 7"	5.00
PERCOLATOR TOPS	- 13/16"	1.00
PERCOLATOR TOPS	- 1"	1.50
PERCOLATOR TOPS	- 2 1/8"	2.00
RELISH SET, SERVING PLATE	- 14"	12.50
RELISH SET, SERVING PLATE (F/G)	- 14"	22.50
RELISH SET, RELISH TRAYS (Ivory)	- 4 ½"	2.00
RELISH SET, RELISH TRAYS(Roy/Rub)-	4½"	5.00
RELISH SET, SAUCE DISH (Forest/G)	- 4"	4.00
RELISH SET, SAUCE DISH (Crystal)	- 4"	3.00

"IVORY OR WHITE TRIMMED WITH 22K GOLD"

DESCRIPTION		CURRENT PRICES
CAKE PLATE, FOOTED (Ivory/White)	- 10"	10.00
SUGAR, SQUARE, (White/Gold Rim)	-	3.00
CREAMER, SQUARE (White/Gold Rim)	-	3.00
RELISH, OVAL, 3 PART	- 11 1/8"	6.00
RELISH, ROUND, 3 PART	- 9 ¾"	8.00
EGG PLATE	- 9 ¾"	10.00
BOWL, FOOTED, SQUARE (White/Gold)	- 8 ½"	8.00
BOWL, SQUARE, FOOTED	- 8 ½"	7.00

DESCRIPTION		CURRENT PRICES

"LUSTRE"

BOWL, NUT	- 5 3/8" —	$4.00
PLATE, NUT	- 6 ¾" —	3.50
VASE	- 7 ¼" —	6.00
SEA SHELL	- 7" —	4.50
ASH TRAY, Tulip	- 4 ½" —	4.00
MAPLE LEAF	- 6 5/8" —	3.00

"MILK WHITE"

BOWL, FOOTED "Vintage"	- 9½"x5½" —	$7.00
CANDY JAR, "Vintage" (Open)	- 5"x6" —	4.00
CANDY JAR, LID "Vintage"	- 7 ¾"x6" —	6.00
WEDDING BOWL/COVER, "Vintage"	7 ½" —	4.00
CAKE PLATE, FOOTED "Vintage"	- 11" —	10.00
BOWL, FOOTED, "Vintage"	- 10" —	8.00
SHERBET, FOOTED	- 5¼" —	3.00
COMPOTE, FOOTED	- 7x3½" —	5.00
BOWL, SERVING "Bubble"	- 8" —	5.00
BOWL, DESSERT "Bubble"	- 4 ½" —	2.00
BOWL, SERVING, "Bubble"	- 11" —	8.00
BOWL, CEREAL, "Bubble	- 5" —	3.00
BASEBALL, 2 pc.	- 3 3/8" dia.—	7.00
GOLF BALL, 2 pc.3	- 3/8" dia. —	7.00
FOOTBALL, 2 pc. (Dark Amber)	- N/A —	10.00
CANDLE CUPS, 10 hr & 15 hr	-	1.00 -2.00
PITCHER	- 12 oz. —	5.00
BOWL, SQUARE	- 6 ½" —	4.00
PLANTER	-7¾x3¼x3 3/8"—	5.00

CANDLE HOLDERS (Pair)	—	$7.00
PLANTERS, FOOTED	- 4"x4 3/8" —	4.00
ASH TRAY, Sq. Flat	—	2.00
ASH TRAY,	—	2.00

"MILK-WHITE HOBNAIL"

PITCHER	- 72 oz. —	$15.00
PITCHER	- 18 oz. —	7.00
TUMBLER	- 9 oz. —	2.00
GOBLET	- 10 oz. —	3.50
GOBLET	- 13 oz. —	2.50
VASE, TALL FOOTED (Ruffled Rim)- 9 ½" tall —	5.00
VASE, Jardiniere	- 4 ¾" —	3.00
VASE, Jardiniere	- 5 ¾" —	4.00
BOWL, HANDLED (Ivory)	-6 ½" —	4.00
DISH, (Cloverleaf, Ivory)	-6 ¾" —	5.00
VASE, BUD	-6 ¾" —	3.00
COOKIE JAR & LID	- 6 ¼" —	15.00

"MISCELLANEOUS"

BOWL, "Leaf & Blossom"	- 4 ¾" —	$6.00
PLATE, "Leaf & Blossom"	- 8" —	5.00
FLOWER POT	- 5"x4" —	4.00
FLOWER PT, (Ivory) Smooth RIM	- 4 ½" —	4.50
VASE, DECO, White	- 5" —	5.00
VASE, DECO, Opaque Blue	- 5" —	12.00
VASE DECO, Fired On Peach	- 5" —	5.00
VASE, DECO, Fired On Blue	- 5" —	12.00

W125

W19

W536

W595

W125— 7¼ x 5⅝" Handled Oblong Tray
W19— 6½"   Square Bowl
W536—10 oz.   Tumbler
W595—12 oz.   Milk or Syrup Pitcher

2 doz. — 13 lbs.
2 doz. — 21 lbs.
3 doz. — 28 lbs.
2 doz. — 21 lbs.

W201/200

W1092

W100

W201/200— 7⅝" Hurricane Lamp ....
   (Milk White Base & Crystal Chimney)
W1092— 6¾" Round Candy Jar & Cover ....
W100—10" Ftd. Cake Plate ....

1 doz. — 11 lbs.

1 doz. — 27 lbs.
½ doz. — 15 lbs.

Milk-White Candleholder is shown on Page 41. See Vases in Milkwhite on Page 48.

20/6

100/520

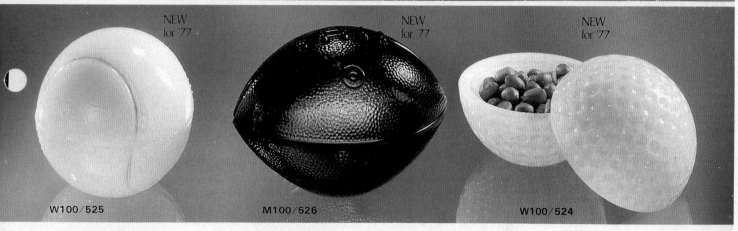

NEW for '77

NEW for '77

NEW for '77

W100/525

M100/526

W100/524

20/6 Crystal DODECAHEDRON 2-Pc. Set. Two pieces—top and bottom sections. Packed in colorful gift carton.
12 sets/17 lbs.

100/520 Crystal SHELL 2-Pc. Set. Top and bottom shell-shape sections. Packed in colorful gift carton.
12 sets/13 lbs.

W100/525 Milk White BASEBALL 2-Pc. Set. Top and bottom baseball-design sections. Packed in colorful gift carton.
12 sets/14 lbs.

M100/526 Harvest Amber® FOOTBALL 2-Pc. Set. Top and bottom football-design sections. Packed in colorful gift carton.
12 sets/15 lbs.

W100/524 Milk White GOLF BALL 2-Pc. Set. Top and bottom golf ball-design sections. Packed in colorful gift carton.
12 sets/13 lbs.

See index for additional listings of Crystal, Milk White and Harvest Amber® gift items.

45

W619

W604

W543

W546

W617

W1664

W1678

MILK-WHITE	CARTON		PRICE
GIFT PACKED	Doz.	Lbs.	Doz.
W619 7½" wedding bowl/cover (004283)	½	10	$6.00
W604 11" footed cake salver/ centerpiece (000851)	⅓	19	16.50
W543 5¼ oz. footed sherbet (004150)	2	17	2.10
W546 7 x 3½" footed compote (004168)	1	16	3.25
W617 10" footed bowl (004267)	⅓	14	12.00
W1664 4½" dessert (001370)	6	24	1.10
W1678 8" bowl (005033)	1	19	2.40

TURQUOISE-BLUE ASH TRAYS

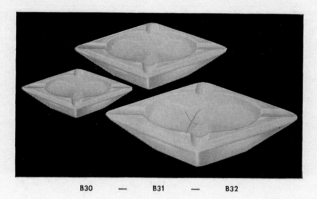

B30 — B31 — B32

PACKING

B30—3½″ Square Ash Tray .... 4 doz. — 15 lbs.
B31—4⅝″ Square Ash Tray .... 2 doz. — 15 lbs.
B32—5¾″ Square Ash Tray .... 1 doz. — 15 lbs.

FOREST GREEN ASH TRAYS

E30 — E31 — E32

E1022

E30—3½″ Ash Tray .... 6 doz. — 21 lbs.
E31—4⅝″ Ash Tray .... 3 doz. — 24 lbs.
E32—5¾″ Ash Tray .... 2 doz. — 33 lbs.
E1022—5¾″ Hexagonal Ash Tray .... 4 doz. — 30 lbs.

MISCELLANEOUS JARS

273 — 274

330

F60

273— ½ Gal. Jar W/1-Pce. Green Cap .... 1 doz. — 19 lbs.
274—1 Gal. Jar W/1-Pce. Green Cap .... 1 doz. — 38 lbs.
330—2½ Gal. Barrel Jar with White Cap & Red Bail .... 1/12 doz. —7½ lbs.
F60—2 Gal. Jar with Metal Cover .... 1/12 doz. — 7 lbs.

Directory on Page 2.

41.

VASES — FLOWER BOWLS

E3302

E3309

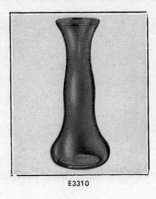

E3310

E3345

PACKING

E3302—3¾"	Bud Vase	4 doz. — 18 lbs.	
E3309—8x4"	Crimped Vase	2 doz. — 20 lbs.	
E3310—9"	Bud Vase	2 doz. — 18 lbs.	
E3345—6⅜"	Vase	4 doz. — 35 lbs.	

E572

M572

W58

W542

E572—9x4⅝"	Vase	1 doz. — 24 lbs.	
M572—9"	Paneled Vase	1 doz. — 23 lbs.	
W58—7¼"	Vase	2 doz. — 29 lbs.	
W542—9½"	Vase	½ doz. — 11 lbs.	

See Page 32 for Crystal Vases and Page 25 for the Crystal "Prescut" Vase.

W555/6136 — W555/6137 — W555/6138
W556/6136 — W556/6137 — W556/6138

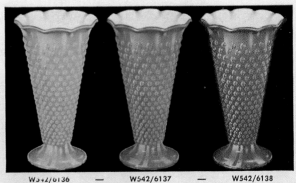

W542/6136 — W542/6137 — W542/6138

W555/6136—4½x4½"	Jardiniere Vase—Yellow	1 doz. — 13 lbs.	
W555/6137—4½x4½"	Jardiniere Vase—Green	1 doz. — 13 lbs.	
W555/6138—4½x4½"	Jardiniere Vase—Coral	1 doz. — 13 lbs.	
W556/6136—5½x5¼"	Jardiniere Vase—Yellow	1 doz. — 18 lbs.	
W556/6137—5½x5¼"	Jardiniere Vase—Green	1 doz. — 18 lbs.	
W556/6138—5½x5¼"	Jardiniere Vase—Coral	1 doz. — 18 lbs.	
W542/6136—9½"	Vase—Yellow	½ doz. — 11 lbs.	
W542/6137—9½"	Vase—Green	½ doz. — 11 lbs.	
W542/6138—9½"	Vase—Coral	½ doz. — 11 lbs.	

33.

MILK WHITE — HOBNAIL DESIGN

W553

W541

W548

W551

PACKING

W553— 9 oz. Water Tumbler	3 doz. — 21 lbs.
W541— 9 oz. Ftd. Goblet	3 doz. — 26 lbs.
W548—72 oz. Pitcher	½ doz. — 19 lbs.
W551—85 oz. Cookie Jar or Ice Tub & Cover	½ doz. — 24 lbs.

CANDLEHOLDER

W984

W984—4 ¾" Candleholder
W14—2 ¼ oz. Oyster Cocktail

PROMOTE SETS

W500/55—7 Pce. Water Set
Each Set in Gift Carton,
6 Sets to Shipping Carton — 43 lbs.
COMPOSITION:
One W548 Pitcher
Six W553 Tumblers

W500/59—7 Pce. Water Set
Each Set in Gift Carton,
6 Sets to Shipping Carton — 50 lbs.
COMPOSITION:
One W548 Pitcher
Six W541 Ftd. Goblets

OYSTER COCKTAIL

W14

2 doz. — 13 lbs.
12 doz. — 19 lbs.

VINTAGE DESIGN

W689

W659

W696

W692

W689—6 oz. Punch Cup		6 doz. — 23 lbs.
W659—9 ½ x 5 ½" Ftd. Bowl		½ doz. — 18 lbs.
W696—5 x 6" Ftd. Candy Jar (No Cover)		1 doz. — 15 lbs.
W692—7 ¾ x 6" Ftd. Candy Jar & Cover		½ doz. — 12 lbs.

The Milk White Punch Set in Vintage Design is shown on Page 30.

IVORY *Fire-King* ® HEAT-PROOF ITEMS

★ W291

★ W1212

W341

PACKING

★ W291—5" Soup or Cereal	4 doz. — 32 lbs.	
★ W1212—8 oz. Coffee Mug	4 doz. — 31 lbs.	
W341—9⅛" Dinner Plate	3 doz. — 39 lbs.	

★ W384 — ★ W327

★ W383 — ★ W327

★ W384—9 oz. St. Denis Cup	4 doz. — 22 lbs.
★ W383—8 oz. Ransom Cup	4 doz. — 22 lbs.
★ W327—5⅞" Saucer	4 doz. — 21 lbs.

WHITE GLASS GIFT PIECES

W40

W41

W42

W40—6" 3-Part Dish	2 doz. — 24 lbs.
W41—6" Footed Dish	2 doz. — 20 lbs.
W42—6" Handled Bowl	2 doz. — 21 lbs.

31.

BARGAINS IN PREPACKED SETS

GOLDEN ANNIVERSARY LINE — 22 K. Gold Trimmed

W4100/57

W4100/57—18 Pce. Luncheon Set

Each Set in Gift Carton, 4 Sets to Shipping Carton—Wt. 41 lbs.
COMPOSITION:

Four W4179/50 Cups	Four W4141/50 Dinner Plates
Four W4129/50 Saucers	One W4153/50 Sugar
Four W4174/50 Desserts	One W4154/50 Creamer

W4100/58—34 Pce. Dinner Set

Each Set in Shipping Carton — Wt. 23 lbs.
COMPOSITION:

Six W4179/50 Cups	One W4178/50 Vegetable Bowl
Six W4129/50 Saucers	One W4147/50 Platter
Six W4174/50 Desserts	One W4153/50 Sugar
Six W4138/50 Salad Plates	One W4154/50 Creamer
Six W4141/50 Dinner Plates	

HEAT-PROOF

W4100/59—52 Pce. Dinner Set

Each Set in Shipping Carton — Wt. 35 lbs.
COMPOSITION:

Eight W4179/50 Cups	Eight W4141/50 Dinner Plates
Eight W4129/50 Saucers	One W4178/50 Vegetable Bowl
Eight W4174/50 Desserts	One W4147/50 Platter
Eight W4138/50 Salad Plates	One W4153/50 Sugar
Eight W4167/50 Soup Plates	One W4154/50 Creamer

See Open Stock Items in this
22 K. Gold Trimmed Line
on Page 11.

HEAT-PROOF JADE-ITE

G3800

G3800—12 Pce. Starter Set

Each Set in Gift Carton, 6 Sets to Shipping Carton — Wt. 49 lbs.
COMPOSITION:

Four G3879 Cups
Four G3829 Saucers
Four G3841 Dinner Plates

See Page 13 for Open Stock Items in Jade-ite.
Jade-ite Mixing Bowls and Refrigerator Items
are on Page 14.

RELISH SET

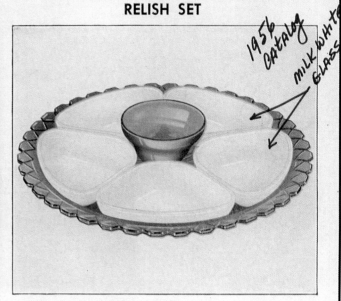

1956 Catalog
MILK WHITE GLASS

E2900/100

E2900/100—7 Pce. Relish Set (Ivory & Forest Green)

Each Set in Individual Gift Box,
6 Sets to Shipping Carton — Wt. 44 lbs.
COMPOSITION:

Five Relish Trays—Ivory
One Service Plate—Forest Green
One Sauce Dish—Forest Green

See Directory on Page 43.

3.

SALT and PEPPER SHAKERS

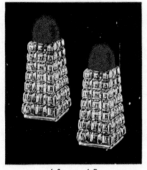

6 S — 6 P

107 S — 107 P

151 S — 151 P

PACKING

6 S—3½" Salt Shaker—Red Plastic Top	6 doz. —	12 lbs.
6 P—3½" Pepper Shaker—Red Plastic Top	6 doz. —	12 lbs.
107 S—3⅞" Salt Shaker—Clear Plastic Top	6 doz. —	13 lbs.
107 P—3⅞" Pepper Shaker—Clear Plastic Top	6 doz. —	13 lbs.
151 S—3⅛" Salt Shaker—Red Plastic Top	6 doz. —	11 lbs.
151 P—3⅛" Pepper Shaker—Red Plastic Top	6 doz. —	11 lbs.

1830 S — 1830 P

2985 S — 2985 P

943 S — 943 P

1830 S—3¼" Salt Shaker—Aluminum Top	6 doz. —	14 lbs.
1830 P—3¼" Pepper Shaker—Aluminum Top	6 doz. —	14 lbs.
2985 S—4¼" Salt Shaker—Aluminum Top	6 doz. —	23 lbs.
2985 P—4¼" Pepper Shaker—Aluminum Top	6 doz. —	23 lbs.
943 S—4¼" Salt Shaker—"Litho" Top	4 doz. —	20 lbs.
943 P—4¼" Pepper Shaker—"Litho" Top	4 doz. —	20 lbs.

RED POLKA DOTS

107-D/5945 — 100/75

107-D/5945—3⅞" Salt & Pepper Shakers	3 dz. Pr. —	14 lbs.
(One Pair to Die-Cut Card)		
100/75—4 Pce. Table Set—Red Polka Dot Dec.	12 sets —	14 lbs.
(Each Set in Printed Gift Box)		

COMPOSITION: One Salt Shaker—Clear Top
One Pepper Shaker—Clear Top
One Cruet with Crystal Stopper

37.

PEACH LUSTRE FANCY WARE
THE NEW METALLIC FINISH THAT SELLS

L58 — 7¼″
VASE
Packs 2 doz.—23 #

L11 — 7″
SHELL DESSERT
Packs 3 doz.—25 #

L847 — 8¼″
FANCY PARTY PLATE
Packs 3 doz.—29 #

L55 — 7½″
CRIMPED BOWL
Packs 2 doz.—25 #

L5069 — 6½″
CRIMPED DISH
Packs 3 doz.—27 #

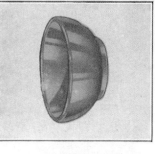

L291 — 5″
BOWL
Packs 4 doz.—32 #

L217 — 6 oz.
BABY MUG
Packs 4 doz.—23 #

PEACH LUSTRE FANCY WARE
THE NEW METALLIC FINISH THAT SELLS

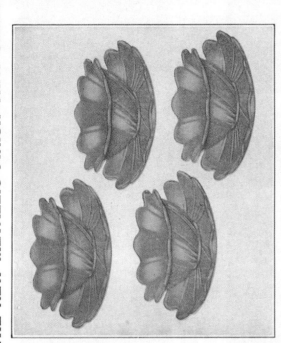

L800/2 — 8 Pce.
PARTY DESSERT SET
Each Set in Gift Ctn.,—12 Sets to R/S Ctn.—52 #
COMPOSITION: Four 5¼″ Desserts
Four 6¾″ Plates

L800/3 — 16 Pce.
PARTY DESSERT SET
Each Set in Gift Ctn., 6 Sets to R/S Ctn.—51 #
COMPOSITION: Eight 5¼″ Desserts
Eight 6¾″ Plates

L800/1 — 2 Pce.
PARTY DESSERT SET
3 doz. Sets Bulk Packed in 2 Ctns.—36 #
COMPOSITION: One 5¼″ Dessert
One 6¾″ Plate

In Peach Lustre Fancy Ware the public is offered for the first time, gold-like finished ware that is a remarkable stride in glass making. The newness of this product with its richness make it a line of great interest and appeal. A wonderful line to feature.

Chip-N-Dip Bowl

Top Row: Candle Warmer with 7 5/8" Splash Proof Bowl, Candle Warmer with 1 ½" Quart Casserole, Candle Warmer with 1 ½ Quart Gold Sprayed Casserole. **Row 2:** Eggnog Punch Bowl Set.

Top Row: Anchorwhite Well & Tree Platter, Ivory Footed Cake Plate, Well & Tree Platter with Gold and Brown Floral Band.
Row 2: Crystal Well & Tree Platter, Crystal Well & Tree Platter with Double Candle Warmer.

MISCELLANEOUS

Listed here are a few of the late finds or unique "FIRE-KING" items that we have run across that just didn't seem to fit in any particular category. We hope that in the future we can find more information on the numerous miscellaneous pieces that we have run across.

The large milk-white with 22K gold trim chip and dip bowl set was introduced in 1964. There is also a 14½" serving plate and an 8" x 12" oval bowl that was part of this set.

The first row of the bottom picture shows some of the many different types of candle warmer sets that were available. The first warmer is quite unusual, the bowl is a milk-white 7 5/8" splashproof bowl with a blue and silver design and came with a polished chrome stand and lid (lid not shown). The second warmer is the most common type used with several of the oval casseroles. It has a brass finish with walnut handles. The third set has an unusual bowl. It's a 1½ qt. crystal casserole that has splattered gold finish on the bowl and a gold, blue and white, Roman style scene on the lid. The second row of the bottom picture is the "EGG NOG" punch bowl set consisting of a 9½" milk-white splashproof bowl and eight small 5 oz. mugs. This set also comes in a "Tom and Jerry" set and a lustre color set.

The third picture shows the various styles of the "Tree and Well" turkey platters and the two candle warmer that was available. In the center of the top row is a footed cake plate that came in ivory or milk-white with 22k gold pattern trim.

PRICE GUIDE		
DESCRIPTION		**CURRENT PRICES**
BOWL, CHIP & DIP	- 11"	— $6.00
BOWL, CHIP & DIP	- 5¼"	— 3.00
BOWL, OVAL	- 8" x 12"	— 5.00
PLATE, SERVER	- 14½"	— 6.00
CANDLE WARMER SETS		
#1-BOWL, WARMER, LID	- 7 5/8" (Bowl)	— 10.00
#2-BOWL, WARMER, LID OVAL	- 1½ qt. cass.	— 15.00
#-BOWL, WARMER, LID ROUND	- 1½ qt. cass.	— 12.00

PRICE GUIDE		
DESCRIPTION		**CURRENT PRICES**
PUNCH BOWL SET		
BOWL, EGG NOG, TOM/JERRY	- 9½"	— $15.00
MUG	- 6 oz.	— 3.50
"WELL & TREE" PLATTER		
PLATTER, Crystal	- 14¾"x10 7/8"	— 10.00
PLATTER, Crystal, Gold Trim	- 14¾"x10 7/8"	— 12.00
PLATTER, Anchorwhite	- 14¾"x10 7/8"	— 15.00
CAKE PLATE	- 11"	— 10.00

General Label
Found On Blue
Bubble, Jane Ray
and Others

To order copies of this book send $24.95 plus $2.95 shipping and handling to:

K & W Collectibles, Inc.
P.O. Box 473
Addison, Al. 35540

Found Only On
Pink Anchorglass
Dinnerware

Found On All
Ivory Dinnerware
and Ovenware

Found Only On
Peach Lustre
Dinnerware, and
Mug & Bowl